Sustainable Land Use and the Food Chain

I0635238

Hans Meliczek
Christoph Kätsch
(*Editors*)

SUSTAINABLE LAND USE AND THE FOOD CHAIN

FROM THE PRODUCER TO THE CONSUMER

Proceedings of the International Seminar held in
Göttingen, Germany

1 – 3 December 2011

ISSDA

International Society for Sustainable Development and Agriculture

Bibliografische Information der Deutschen Nationalbibliothek

Die Deutsche Nationalbibliothek verzeichnet diese Publikation in der
Deutschen Nationalbibliografie; detaillierte bibliografische Daten sind im Internet
über http://dnb.d-nb.de abrufbar.
1. Aufl. - Göttingen : Cuvillier, 2012

978-3-95404-191-6

© CUVILLIER VERLAG, Göttingen 2012
   Nonnenstieg 8, 37075 Göttingen
   Telefon: 0551-54724-0
   Telefax: 0551-54724-21
   www.cuvillier.de

1. Auflage, 2012
Gedruckt auf säurefreiem Papier

978-3-95404-191-6

Foreword

The continuous growth of the world population has provoked concerns and apprehension about future global food supply. While there is still scope for enhancing plant and animal production through modern production and management technologies, the long-term viability of our current food production system is increasingly being questioned because of the ongoing depletion of natural resources including soil degradation, monoculture, excessive use of fertilizers and pesticides, inappropriate irrigation techniques and environmental pollution. In order to sustain food supplies it is important to minimize these deficiencies, improve the inherent potential of crops and animals for efficient use of inputs, use improved agro-technologies and apply sustainable land use patterns. In addition, the reduction of post-harvest losses and food losses at the consumer level is an equally important means to stabilize the world food security situation.

As a contribution to the ongoing discussion on world food security the International Society for Sustainable Development and Agriculture (ISSDA) organized in Göttingen, Germany from 1 to 3 December 2011 an International Seminar on Sustainable Land Use and the Food Chain: From the Producer to the Consumer. This book is based on the research findings presented at the seminar. It was attended by scientists from 16 countries. Their contributions cover a wide range of subjects such as technologies for sustainable wheat production, genetic options for wheat production, and phosphorus uptake of wheat as well as more general topics such as organic farming, land use patterns, life cycle assessment, safe drinking water, food quality control, gender equality, rice trade, vegetable supply chain and the contribution of plant and animal breeders for sustainable agriculture. One paper reviews the food security situation in intervals of 30 years from 1864 to 2014 with a perspective to 2044 and 2074. The geographical areas covered by the papers extend from Benin, Germany, India, Indonesia, Timor Leste and Pakistan to South Africa.

The seminar was the first major initiative of the International Society for Sustainable Development and Agriculture. It was established in January 2011 with the objective to establish and promote an international forum for researchers and development specialists concerned with natural resources including agriculture, forestry and other disciplines related to sustainable development.

The editors express their sincere gratitude to the authors who have contributed their papers for publication. They also thank Mr. Altaf Hussain, Dr. Asif Abdul Rahman, Mr. Bhumi Verma, Dr. Manfred Kern, Prof. Dr. Wolfgang Merbach, and Dr. Johanna Schott for their support in organizing the Seminar. Special thanks go to Bayer Crop Science for their generous sponsorship.

Hans Meliczek, Christoph Kätsch

Editors

Contents

Enhancing Phosphorus Uptake and Use Efficiency in Wheat for Sustainable Crop Production – Management and Genetic Options

R. K. Behl[1], Dinisha Abhishek[3], Ashwani Kumar[1], A. K. Chhabra[1], S. K. Sethi[1] and Neeru Narula[2],

[1] Department of Genetics and Plant-Breeding, [2]Department of Microbiology, CCS Haryana Agricultural University, Hisar, India, [3] Institut fuer Gemuese- und Zierpflanzenbau, Grossbeeren, Germany

Abstract

Wheat, the second major cultivated food crop worldwide requires phosphorus (P) for its physiological and biochemical accomplishments. Phosphorus, a key element in the nutrient supply chain realizes a potential yield of wheat crop. Enhancement of P acquisition and utilization by plants is critical for economic, humanitarian and ecological reasons (Vance et al., 2003). Conservation strategies for P utilization include: development of P efficient cultivars and integrated application of inorganic P sources through highly soluble fertilizers coupled with biofertilizers such as arbuscular mycorrhizal fungi, and rhizobacteria like *Azotobacter*, which in turn will help in solubilizing phosphorus in rhizosphere and promote its uptake by plants.

In a study conducted earlier, thirty wheat genotypes were classified into eight different groups on the basis of their grain yield performance and P uptake which proved useful in identifying varieties suitable for cultivation in different soil P regimes and selection of parents for recombination breeding to develop P efficient cultivars. It was concluded that inter-mating between varieties belonging to HGY-HP (PBW 343 and WH 711) and HGY-LP (Raj 3765 and WH 283) would further expand genotypic variability and thus the frequency of recombinants exhibiting different grain yield and P uptake levels.

Background

Wheat, the second most cultivated crop worldwide provides 21 percent of the food calorie and 20 percent of the protein for more than 4.5 billion people in 94 developing countries (Braun et al., 2010). Phosphorus is a key substrate in energy metabolism in the form of ATP, biosynthesis of nucleic acid in the form of sugar-phosphate backbone and membranes in the form of a phospholipid bilayer. Thus, required to sustain plant life, P affects wheat growth and development throughout the season. An adequate amount of P improves wheat seedling establishment, encourages early season development of adventurous roots, improves winter hardiness and facilitates greater nitrogen uptake which results in higher grain protein.

Abundant P results in early proliferation of tillers which increases biomass and grain yield potential (Behl et al., 2005). Also, wheat with adequate P matures earlier and more uniformly. The uneven development in a global economy has contributed to the uneven distribution of P in agricultural soils of the world. Generous application of high-grade phosphorus fertilizers, following more than half a century, agricultural soils in Europe and North America now said to have surpassed critical phosphorus levels and thus requires light application to replace what is lost in the harvest (FAO, 2006). However, the situation in developing and emerging economies is contrastingly different (Cordell et al., 2009). There will be an estimated 2-2.5 billion new mouths to feed by 2050 (IWMI, 2006), mainly in urban slums of the developing world. For securing food, the need for P fertilization in the growing economies like India and China is expected to increase in the foreseeable future (Maene, 2007). Phosphorus fertilizers, derived from high grade rock phosphate reserves are non-renewable finite resources (Vance, 2001). The unique property of P to form insoluble complexes with free iron and aluminium oxides in acidic soil of tropical and subtropical agriculture and with calcium and magnesium compounds in calcareous soil, results in usually very low recovery (10-30 percent) of P fertilizer by crop plants (Holford, 1997). This warrants for more sustainable use of P resources in agriculture and improving the efficiency of P fertilizers used in different agricultural systems (Cordell et al., 2009), to extend the world P availability.

Developing P efficient cultivars (yield well under P deficient conditions) are not in themselves a sustainable solution to the problem, as it will not deny the ultimate need for P fertilizers (Sanchez, 2010). However, it is the most realistic approach to the problem of P deficiency in cultivated soil (Gunes et al., 2006; Liao et al., 2008). More P efficient cultivars provide opportunities for initial gain in crop productivity to be achieved that may consequently assist access to P fertilizers (Lynch, 2007).The distribution of improved cultivars to farmers is among the most cost-effective means to upgrade crop production (Byerlee, 1996). In this paper we review mechanisms underlying phosphorus uptake and transport in wheat plant and the potential of different approaches that leads to improved P use efficiency in agricultural systems.

How P is absorbed by wheat?

Wheat being a cereal produces two types of roots : seminal roots (also called as primary roots) develop at the nodes of the embryonic hypocotyl of the germinating cross and adventurous roots (also called nodal, secondary or crown roots) emerge from nodes at the base of the apical culm (main stem) and tillers only when the fourth main stem leaf appears. The roots generally considered as source of Pi for other plant parts, become a sink during Pi starvation. This appears to be a deliberate, adaptive response by the plant to promote root proliferation and thereby enhance soil exploration and Pi uptake (Raghothama, 1999). High-input semi-dwarf wheat is characterized by shallow root architecture i.e. seminal root dependence. In contrast, low input genotypes develop a large root system essentially based on adventurous roots.

Plant roots absorb inorganic P (Pi), from the soil solution mainly in the form of primary orthophosphate $(H_2PO_4)^{2-}$ and secondary orthophosphate $(HPO_4)^{2-}$ ions (Vance et al., 2003). Many other forms are also available. Soil phosphate ions move towards the root via diffusion (Marschner, 1995).Plants must maintain intercellular (cytosol) Pi level at millimolar range, even when the concentration of soil Pi are at micromolar level, to meet the high demand of Pi in the cells (Reisenauer,1966). This necessitates roots to acquire Pi against a strong concentration gradient (100- fold or higher). An energy mediated H^+/Pi co-transport process, driven by the plasma membrane H^+ extrusion pump such as the P-type H^+ATPase has been proposed for Pi uptake in plants (Ullrich-Eberius et al., 1981; Ullrich-Eberius et al., 1984). Two categories of transporters are expressed for phosphate acquisition and transport across

4

the plants. High-affinity P transporters primarily involved in P acquisition from external soil solution to the cell cytoplasm and the low-affinity P transporters also involve in P uptake and vascular loading and unloading, internal distribution and remobilization of acquired P (Smith et al., 2001). Acquisition of P by high-P- affinity transporters is regulated by internal P in the plants whereas low-affinity transport system expressed constitutively. Phosphate acquired by root epidermal cells through the transporter mediated pathway and apoplasmic movement is loaded into the xylem for further transportation in different plant parts according to metabolic needs (Bieleski and Ferguson, 1983). The initial movement of the phosphate ions across the plasma membrane to the root epidermal cells and cortical cells and subsequent loading into xylem appears to be two major checkpoints of the regulation of ion transport across roots (Smith et al., 2003). Plants have developed adaptive responses to facilitate external Pi acquisition, limit consumption of Pi and adjust recycling internally to maintain constant cytoplasmic Pi concentration referred to as homeostasis, in case of inadequate Pi availability (Raghothama, 1999; Poirier and Bucher, 2002).

In wheat full length cDNA sequence of a high affinity phosphate transporter gene (*PHT1*), *TaPHT1.2* and partial sequence of seven other *PHT1*genes were cloned (Davies et al., 2002). A 579 bp of *TaPHT1.2* promoter is sufficient to drive gene expression in the roots of wheat and *Arabidopsis* under low P conditions (Tittarelli et al., 2007). The regulatory element in Pi response, P1BS, is also identified in *TaPHT1.2* transporter, *TaPHT1.2-D,* on long arm of wheat 4D (Miao et al., 2009).

Approaches for improving phosphorus use efficiency in wheat

Use efficiency of P (PUE) depends on external P availability and internal P requirements. The latter can be split into P uptake efficiency (Fohse et al., 1988) and P utilization efficiency. Phenotypic and genotypic adaptations influencing P acquisition under P stress mainly involve changes in root characteristics because of relative immobility of P in soil, with the highest concentration usually found in the top soil. Increased harvest index, P harvest index and low P.

P concentration in grain may improve P utilization efficiency in wheat (Batten, 1992). Being in additive mode, small optimization of the each component traits can trigger PUE of wheat as a whole. Achieving these changes can be brought about through the following approaches described below.

Screening and breeding of P efficient wheat lines.

Selection of P efficient lines in terms of yield is complicated as almost everything in the genome contributes either directly or indirectly to yield. If the selection pressure for P or any other nutrient is strong enough then efficient genotypes may be selected based on yield, but there will be possibility of the strong influence of interactions that would affect the results under field conditions (Ortiz-Monasterio et al., 2001). Screening is further complicated in the field because of the uneven distribution of P. Genotypes can be screened in uniform soils under greenhouse experiment. However, growing conditions are less realistic and ranking may not be closely related to P efficiency obtained in the field (Gunes et al., 2006). Special attention should be given to growth conditions in screening wheat for P efficiency. Green house experiments however, can act as a primary screening tool to reduce the number of genotypes.

The geometry of the root system is essential for improvement of P uptake as it may be directed to maximize root per unit soil volume i.e. root length density. Wheat genotypes with higher root length density are able to take up more P (Manske et al., 2000a). Root diameter, root hair abundance (Jones et al., 1989) and high ratio of root to shoot growth-rates (Fohse et al., 1988) are other determinants of P uptake efficiency in wheat. Genotypes with thinner roots showed improved P uptake (Manske et al., 1996). Manipulation in root hair morphology is the least metabolically costly way of increasing root surface area. Root hair length plays a significant role in P acquisition (Gahoonia et al., 1997). Root hair density among bread wheat varied considerably and positively correlated with P uptake at anthesis when grown on a P deficient calcareous Ardisols (Manske, 1997). Wide genotypic variation and heritability of root morphology, root hair length and density provide opportunities for selection and breeding for root characteristics for increasing P acquisition (Gahoonia and Nielsen, 2004).

Root induces changes in the PH of their rhizosphere, which affects the bioavailability of soil P (Grinsted et al., 1983). The concentration of orthophosphate ions in the soil solution is pH influenced. Plant species or genotypes inducing rhizosphere acidification may absorb more P by this mechanism (Gahoonia and Nielsen, 2004). Organic acids especially citrate and malate ions are the major wheat roots exudates responsible for this adaptation (Manske and Vlek, 2002; Khademi et al., 2010).The consumption of organic acid by the microorganisms might reduce their effectiveness in dissolving strongly bound P in rhizosphere soil. However, as long as there is net presence of organic acids (i.e. more produced than consumed) they will be useful in mobilising P from strongly bound P pools (Gahoonia and Nielsen, 2004). Exudation promotes the solubility of soil P from inorganic and adsorbed P fractions (Neumann and Romheld, 1999). Under conditions of Fe deficiency, roots release considerable amounts of chelating exudates (phytosiderophores), which form plant-available Fe-phytosiderophore complexes (Aciksoz et al., 2011) and thus release bound Pi from the Fe-P complex, in to the rhizosphere. Depending on the soil type organic P may constitute 30-80 percent of the total phosphorus (Dalal, 1977). Plants can only absorb organic P compounds after they are hydrolyzed to inorganic P, preferably close to the root surface in order to prevent sorption by the soil particles. Organic P can be digested by root-surface-bound or excreted phosphatase (Seeling and Jungk, 1996). Genotypic variation in root phosphatase, excreted or bound at the root surface, exists (McLachlan, 1980). Results from a set of genotype also indicate the ability of wheat roots to utilize organic P through root phosphatase activity (Tabatabai and Bremner, 1969).

Root modification systems however, usually require additional carbon input. In wheat over 50 percent of the carbohydrate are translocated to roots for root growth and maintenance and for the absorption of ions, of them anion uptake only costs about 20 percent of the translocated carbohydrate (Manske and Vlek, 2002). If the demand for carbohydrates in large root systems is not compensated for by improved P and water acquisition, as in case of sufficient nutrient and water supply, the roots themselves may limit yield (Manske et al., 2001) and study of wheat root traits may be very labour intensive. Techniques like minirhizotron, image analysis system and root washing machines have been developed and although they are often precise and faster, they are expensive and unsuitable for screening large number of segregating population (Manske et al., 2001). Indirect selection for above ground traits related to root growth could be a possibility to select genotypes with improved root systems for low input conditions. The number of spikes m^2 is positively correlated with root length density, especially at low P (Manske et al., 2000a). Nonetheless, assessing root traits is essential for improving P acquisition efficiency under low P conditions, root analysis of large population can be done in nutrient solution. Hayes et al., (2004), by using only two wheat cultivars concluded that screening in nutrient solution is not reliable for P efficiency differences found in soil culture.

On the other hand, in a glasshouse comparison of 73 types of bread wheat and durum wheat, at similar concentrations of shoot P, genotypes showed considerable variation in shoot dry weight (Ozturk et al., 2005) suggesting useful variation in internal P utilization efficiency. More effective translocation of assimilates into kernels may improve the P utilization (Horst et al., 1996) because developing kernels are strong sink for assimilates. Given the small margin to breed for higher harvest index (HI), selection for low grain P content may improve P utilization efficiency. Selection for wheat genotypes that removes small amounts of P from the soil due to their low P grain concentration can contribute to sustainable land use (Schulthess et al., 1997). Opportunity exists to manipulate P grain composition. Nearly all the genotypic variations in seed total P are due to a variation in phytate, a mixed cation salt of phytic acid. Non-phytate P tends to remain constant (Raboy et al., 1991; Raboy, 2003). High phytate grain concentration reduces P bioavailability in monogastric animals and also contributes to poor availability of essential micronutrients (Liu et al., 2006). However, low P in seed can impact on seedling establishment (Bolland and Baker, 1988; Derrick and Ryan, 1998) especially under low input P conditions and agronomic involvements like P seed enrichment or P placement (Rebafka et al., 1993; Sekiya and Yano, 2010) may be required to overcome any restrictions to seedling growth. Moreover, more detailed experiments are needed for better understanding of role of P translocation within the plants and re-translocation to meristems (Ozturk et al., 2005) and to grain in improved P efficiency in wheat.

Any wheat breeding programme for higher grain yield, selects indirectly for improved P utilization (Egle et al., 1999), especially under low P regimes. Modern breeding had increased P use efficiency through better utilization for grain formation i.e. higher P harvest index (Horst et al., 1993), further improvement in P use efficiency can be realized by increasing either ears per plant or grains per ear (Wang et al., 2010). In a Metroglyph analysis of spring wheat Gill et al. (2004), classified 30 genotypes in to eight different groups on the basis of their grain yield performance and phosphorus uptake and concluded: low P requiring genotypes can be grown on soils marginally deficient in available P to get maximum phosphate use efficiency which in turn results in better cost benefit ratio; Inter-mating between varieties belonging to high grain yield-high phosphorus (HGY-HP; PBW 343 and WH 711) and high grain yield-low phosphorus (HGY-LP; Raj 3765 and WH 283) group would further expand genotypic variability and thus frequency of recombinants exhibiting different grain yield and P uptake levels.

Breeding of new improved cultivar relies on screening of genotypes varying considerably for associated traits. As, traits most likely associated with P use efficiency has been identified in wheat, it seems feasible to combine root traits and internal P utilization efficiency into agronomically elite commercial cultivars and perform early generation selection under both low and high P conditions. The later will select for high yield potential and former for adaptation to low P (Manske et al., 2000a). Phenotypic complexity of roots and shoot responses to P limiting conditions reflects the polygenic nature of the process. Variation for complex phenotypic traits are frequently controlled by many genetic loci, scattered throughout the genome (Price, 2006). Quantitative trait loci analysis is based on statistically significant association of phenotypic differences for the trait of interest with molecular markers that constitute the genetic map (Doerge, 2001). Molecular markers found linked to the target trait can be used in marker-assisted selection (for reviews, see Gupta et al., 1999; Varshney et al., 2007) as given challenges and the time scale, breeding for improved cultivars can no longer rely on 10-year cycles and all technologies that shorten selection cycles must be mobilized (Paux et al., 2011). Despite QTLs related to P deficiency tolerance has been identified in wheat (Su et al. 2006, 2009; Li et al. 2007; Guo et al., 2011) their utilization in marker aided selection is a remaining challenge.

Transgenic approach

Exudation of organic acids and phosphatase into the rhizophere has been proposed to increase P acquisition efficiency (PAE) in wheat plants. Transgenic barley expressing *TaALMT1* aluminium activated malate transporter gene, enhanced expression of which improved Al^{3+} resistance in transgenic wheat (Pereira et al., 2010), showed improved P nutrition and grain production when grown on an acidic soil (Delhaize et al., 2009). These finding provides an opportunity to manipulate P deficiency and aluminium toxicity tolerance in wheat under acidic soil using *TaALMT1* as a candidate. Phytases, a special type of APases with the capability to hydrolyze phytate and its derivates, predominant inositol phosphates present in seeds and soil. Wheat engineered for *Aspergillus* phytase-encoding gene (phyA), accumulates significant amount of *Aspergillus* phytase in grains may be of relevance for improving the phytate-phosphorus digestibility in non-ruminants including humans. Given soluble P, high affinity phosphate transporters play an important role in Pi uptake and translocation (Zeng et al., 2002; Davies et al., 2002; Tittarelli et al., 2007; Miao et al., 2009) and offer the possibility to enhance the P nutrition of wheat by gene technology approach.

Integrated approach

An integrated approach that enhances availability and acquisition of native P includes integrated use of inorganic P sources through highly soluble fertilizers coupled with inoculation of plant growth promoting rhizobacteria (PGPR) like *Azotobacter*, *Azospirrilum* or mycorrhizae (Fig 1).

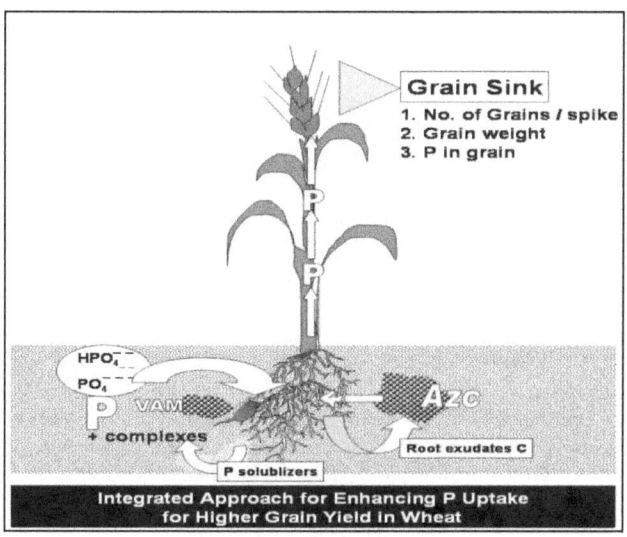

Fig.1, adopted from Behl et al., 2005

This approach can also compliment the products of plant breeding and gene technology besides improving the efficiency of applied P fertilizers. PGPR enhance the capacity of plants to acquire P from soil through the various mechanisms includes: increased lateral root growth by hormonal stimulation like production of indole-3-acetic acid (IAA) (Barbieri et al., 1986), gibberellin or enzymes that alter plant ethylene precursors such as ACC-deaminase (Richardson et al., 2009; Hayat et al., 2010), solubilization and mineralization of fixed P from inorganic and organic forms via efflux of organic anions and protons, production of sidero-phores and release of phosphatase (Richardson et al., 2009). Genotypic differences for *Azotobacter* infection (Kumar and Narula, 1999) increase P (Kumar et al., 2001) and micro-nutrients uptake (Singh et al., 2004) exists among Indian bread wheat. Solubilized P can be absorbed both directly by plants or *via* arbuscular mycorrhizal fungal hyphae. Mycorrhizal symbiosis is based on the mutulastic exchange of carbon from the host plant in return for P (Schweiger and Jakobsen, 2000) and other nutrients from the fungus (Marschner and Dell, 1994).Wheat roots excrete carbonaceous exudates which could help in proliferation of VAM and *Azotobacter chroococcum* (Azc) (Manske et al., 2000b). Inoculation of Azc also compliments wheat-VAM interaction due to its nitrogen fixation, phytohormone production and phosphate solubilizing properties (Behl et al., 2003). Thus, inoculation of VAM with phytohormone and vitamin producing Azc could result in improved plant growth promoting effects of diazotrophs in rhizosphere. Behl et al., (2003), reported the effect of cultivar and dual inoculation of Azc and arbuscular mycorrhiza fungi (AMF, *Glomus fascicula-tum*) on AMF infection in four wheat varieties and their three crosses under low input condi-tions. Comparative evaluation of treatment averages viz. control (common in other two treatments also), AMF and AMF + Azc revealed that inoculation of Azc led to increase in AMF infection in roots.

High-affinity phosphate transporters localized in root-mycorrhiza interface in cortical cells, co-ordinately expressed in response to P deficiency and interaction with mycorrhizal fungi in wheat (Glassop et al., 2005; Bucher, 2007). However, this information requires further basic research for better understanding of mechanism underlying mycorrhizal Pi uptake pathways, for adoption in breeding programme. Regardless of substantial potential, with an exception of commercialization of fungal-based inoculants in North America and recently in Europe and Australia, large scale application of microbial products remains limited due to inconsistent response to inoculants under different environments as a consequence of complex plant-microbe interaction in soil environment which has proven difficult to manage (Richardson, 2001; Richardson and Simpson, 2011).

Conclusion and Outlook

P nutrition is critical for reaching the attainable yield potential of wheat. Given that genetic variability exists among bread wheat genotypes and alien species, there is some scope for pyramiding genes for P acquisition and utilization in agronomically superior genotypes possessing commensurate ontogenic and structural features to support sinks for grain yield with efficient use of Pi, through combination of conservation strategies discussed in this review. Plant breeding under the umbrella of Plant Genomics will lead to the identification of genes regulating adaptation to P stress through the development of well-defined Recombinant Inbred Lines (RILs) and Near Isogenic Lines (NILs) having QTLs for P tolerance coupled with next generation sequencing (Vance, 2010). P nutrition must be a part of an integrated nutrient management strategy that considers the importance of bio-inoculants, organic manures and other nutrients.

References

Aciksoz, S. B., Ozturk, L., Gokmen, O. O., Romheld, V. and Cakmak, I.: Effect of nitrogen on root release of phytosiderophores and root uptake of Fe (III)-phytosiderophore in Fe-deficient wheat plants. Physiol Plantarum 142: 287-296, 2011.

Barbieri, P., Zanelli, T. and Galli, E.: Wheat inoculation with Azospirillum brasilence Sp6 and some mutants altered in nitrogen fixation and indole-3-acetic acid. FEMS Microbiol Lett 36: 87-90, 1986.

Batten, G. D.: A review of phosphorus efficiency in wheat. Plant Soil 146: 163-168, 1992.

Behl, R. K., Lokesh, Chhabra, A. K., Narula, N., Singh and Punia, M. S.: Enhancing phosphorus uptake and use efficiency in wheat breeding for input use efficiency. In: .Breeding Crops for Input Use Efficency, Behl, R. K., Waldia, R. S. and Chhabra, A. K. (eds), Department of Plant Breeding, CCS HAU, Hisar, 128-136, 2005.

Behl, R. K., Sharma, H., Kumar, V. and Singh K. P.: Effect of dual inoculation of VA Mycorrhiza and *Azotobacter chroococcum* on above flag leaf characters in wheat. Arch Agron Soil Scie 49: 25-31, 2003.

Bieleski, R. L. and Ferguson, I. B.: Physiology and metabolism of phosphate and its compounds. In: Lauch, li. A., Bieleski, R., L. (eds): Encyclopedia of plant physiology, NS, Vol 15A. Springer, Berlin, Heidelberg, New York, 422–449, 1983.

Bolland, M. D. A. and Baker, M. J.: High phosphorus concentrations in seed of wheat and annual medic are related to higher rates of dry matter production of seedlings and plants. Aust J Exp Agric 28: 765–770, 1988.

Bucher, M.: Functional biology of plant phosphate uptake at root and mycorrhiza interfaces. New Phytol 173: 11–26, 2007.

Byerlee, D.: Modern Varieties, Productivity, and Sustainability: Recent Experience and Emerging Challenges. World Development 24: 697-718, 1996.

Braun, H., J., Atlin, G. and Payne, T.: Multi-location testing as a tool to identify plant response to global climate change. In: Reynolds, M. P. (ed.), Climate change and crop production. Wallingford, UK: CABI Publishers, 115-138, 2010.

Cordell, D., Drangert, J. O. and White, S.: The story of phosphorus: Global food security and food for thought. Global Environ Chang 19: 292–305, 2009.

Dalal, R. C.: Soil organic phosphorus. Adv Agron 29: 83-117, 1977.

Davies, T. G. E., Ying, J., Xu, Q., Li, Z. S., Li, J. Y. and Gordon-Weeks, R.: Expression analysis of putative high-affinity phosphate transporters in Chinese winter wheats. Plant Cell Environ 25: 1325-1340, 2002.

Delhaize, E., Taylor, P., Hocking, P. J., Simpson, R. J., Ryan, P. R. and Richardson, A. E.: Transgenic barley (HordeumvulgareL.) expressing the wheat aluminium resistance gene (TaALMT1) shows enhanced phosphorus nutrition and grain production when grown on an acid soil. Plant Biotechnol J 7: 391–400, 2009.

Derrick, J. W. and Ryan, M. H.: Influence of seed phosphorus content on seedling growth in wheat: Implications for organic and conventional farm management in South East Australia. Biol Agric Horticul 16: 223–237, 1998.

Doerge, R.: Mapping and analysis of quantitative trait loci in experimental populations. Nat Rev Gen 3: 43–52, 2001.

Egle, K., Manske, G., Romer, W. and Vlek, P. L. G.: Improved phosphorus efficiency of three new wheat genotypes from CIMMYT in comparison with an older Mexican variety. J Plant Nutr Soil Sci 162: 353-358, 1999.

FAO: Plant Nutrition for Food Security: A Guide for Integrated Nutrient Management, FAO Fertilizer and Plant Nutrition Bulletin 16. Food and Agriculture Organization of the United Nations, Rome, 2006.

Fohse, D., Classen, N. and Jungk, A.: Phosphorus efficiency of plants. I. External and internal P requirement and P uptake efficiency of different plant species. Plant Soil 11: 101-109, 1988.

Gahoonia, T. S. and Nielsen, N. E.: Root traits as tools for creating phosphorus efficient crop varieties. Plant Soil 260: **47-57**, 2004.

Gahoonia, T. S., Care, D. and Nielsen, N. E.: Root hairs and phosphorus acquisition of wheat and barley cultivars. Plant Soil 191: 181-188, 1997.

Gill, H. S., Singh, A., Sethi, S. K. and Behl, R. K., Phosphorus uptake and use efficiency in different varieties of bread wheat (Triticum aestivum L) Arch Agron Soil Sci 50: 563-572, 2004.

Glassop, D., Smith, S.E. and Smith, F. W.: Cereal phosphate transporters associated with the mycorrhizal pathway of phosphate uptake into roots. Planta 222: 688-698, 2005.

Grinsted, M. J., Hedley, M. J., Nye, P. H. and White, R. E.: Plant induced changes in the rhizosphere of rape (*Brassica napus* var. Emerald) seedlings. I pH change and the increase in P concentration in the soil solution. New Phytol 91: 19-29, 1983.

Gunes, A., Inal, A., Alpaslan, M. and Cakmak, I.: Genotypic variation in phosphorus efficiency between wheat cultivars grown under greenhouse and field conditions. Soil Sci Plant Nutri 52: 470-478, 2006.

Guo, Y., Kong, Fan-mei, Xu, Yun-feng, Zhao, Y., Liang, X., Wang, Ying-ying, An Diao-guo Li, and Si-shen: QTL mapping for seedling traits in wheat grown under varying concentrations of N, P and K nutrients. Theor Appl Genet DOI 10.1007/s00122-011-1749-7, 2011.

Gupta, P. K., Varshney, R. K., Sharma, P. C. and Ramesh, B.: Molecular markers and their applications in wheat breeding. Plant Breedi 118: 369–390, 1999.

Hayat, R., Ali, S., Amara, U., Khalid. R. and Ahmed, I.: Soil beneficial bacteria and their role in plant growth promotion: a review. Ann Microbiol 60: 579–598, 2010.

Hayes, J. E., Zhu, Y.-G., Mimura, T. and Reid, R. J.: An assessment of the usefulness of solution culture in screening for phosphorus efficiency in wheat. Plant Soil 261: 91-97, 2004.

Holford, I. C. P.: Soil phosphorus its measurements and its uptake by plants. Aust J Soil Res 35: 227-239, 1997.

Horst, W. J., Abdou, M. and Wiesler, F.: Genotypic differences in phosphorus efficiency of wheat. Plant Soil 155-156: 293–296, 1993.

Horst, W. J., Abdou, M. and Wiesler, F.: Differences between wheat cultivars in acquisition and utilization of phosphorus. Z Pflanzenernahr Bodenk 159:155-161, 1996.

IWMI: Comprehensive assessment of water management in agriculture. Cosponsers: FAO, CGIAR, CBD, Ramsar, 2006.

Jones, G. P. D., Blair, G. J. and Jessop, R. S.: Phosphorus efficiency in wheat-a useful selection criteria. Field Crops Res 21: 257-264, 1989.

Khademi, Z., Jones, D. L., Malakouti, M. J. and Asadi, F.: Organic acids differ in enhancing phosphorus uptake by *Triticum aestivum* L.-effects of rhizosphere concentration and counterion. Plant Soil 334:151-159, 2010.

Kumar, V., Behl, R. K. and Narula, N.: Establishment of phosphate solubilizing strains of *Azotobacter chroococcum*in the rhizosphere and their effect on wheat cultivars under green house conditions. Microbial Res 156: 87-94, 2001.

Kumar, V. and Narula, N.: Solubilization of inorganic phosphates and growth emergence of wheat as affected by *Azotobacter chroococcum* mutants. Biol Fertil Soils 28: 301-305, 1999.

Li, Z. X., Ni, Z. F., Peng, H. R., Liu, Z. Y., Nie, X. L., Xu, S. B., Liu, G. and Sun, Q. X.: Molecular mapping of QTLs for root response to phosphorus deficiency at seedling stage in wheat (*Triticumaestivum* L.). Prog Nat Sci 17: 1177–1184, 2007.

Liao, M., Hocking, P. J., Dong, B., Delhaize, E., Richardson, A. E. and Ryan, P. R.: Genotypic variation in phosphorus efficiency among wheat genotypes grown on two contrasting Australian soils. Aust J Agr Res 59: 157–166, 2008.

Liu, Z. H., Wang, H. Y., Wang, X. E., Zhang, G. P., Chen, P. D. and Liu, D. J.: Genotypic and spike positional difference in grain phytase activity, phytate, inorganic phosphorus, iron, and zinc contents in wheat (*Triticumaestivum* L.) J Cereal Sci 44: 212–219, 2006.

Lynch, J. P.: Roots of the second green revolution. Aust J Bot 55: 1–20, 2007.

Maene, L. M.: International Fertilizer Supply and Demand. In: Australian Fertilizer Industry Conference, International Fertilizer Industry Association, August, 2007.

Manske, G. G. B.: Utilization of the genotypic variability of VAM -symbiosis and root length density in breeding phosphorus efficient wheat cultivars at CIMMYT. Final report of a special project. Mexico City: CIMMYT, 1997.

Manske, G. G. B., Ortiz-Monasterio, J. I., Van Ginkel, M., Gonzalez, R., Rajaram, S., Molina, E. and Vlek, P. L. G.: Traits associated with improved P-uptake efficiency in CIMMYT's semi dwarf spring bread wheat grown on an acid Andisol in Mexico. Plant Soil 221:189-204, 2000a.

Manske, G. G. B., Ortiz-Monasterio, J. I., Van Ginkel, M., Gonzalez, R. and Vlek, P. L. G.: Phosphorus uptake, utilization efficiency and grain yield of semidwarf wheat grown in acid or alkaline, P deficient soils. 5th International Wheat Conference, June 10-14, Ankara, Turkey, 1996.

Manske, G. G. B., Ortiz-Monasterio, J. I. and Vlek, P. L. G.: Techniques for measuring genetic diversity in roots. In: Reynolds, M. P., Ortiz-Monasterio, J. I. and McNab, A. (eds), Application of physiology in wheat breeding. Mexico, D.F., CIMMYT, 208-218, 2001.

Manske, G. G. B. and Vlek, P. L. G.: Root Architecture-Wheat as a Model Plant. In: Waisel, Y. and Eshel, A. (eds), Plant roots the hidden half. Marcel Dekker, Inc, New York. Basel, 249-259, 2002.

Manske, G. G. B., Behl, R. K., Luttger, A. B. and Vlek, P. L. G.: Enhancement of mycorrhizal infection, nutrient efficiency and plant growth by *Azotobacter chroococcum* in wheat: Evidence of varietal effects. In: Narula, N. (ed), *Azotobacter* in sustainable agriculture. CBS Publishers and Distributors, New Delhi, p136-147, 2000b.

Marschner, H.: Mineral Nutrition of Higher Plants. 2nd edn. Academic Press, London, 1995.

Marschner, H, and Dell, B.: Nutrientuptake in mycorrhizalsymbiosis. Plant Soil 159: 89-102, 1994.

McLachlan, K. D.: Acid phosphatase activity of intact roots and phosphorus nutrition in plants. 1. Assay conditions and phosphatase activity. Aust J Agric Res 31: 429–440, 1980.

Miao, J., Sun, J., Liu, D., Li, B., Zhang, A., Li, Z. and Tong, Y.: Characterization of the promoter of phosphate transporter *TaPHT1.2* differentially expressed in wheat varieties. J Genet Genomics 36: 455-466, 2009.

Neumann, G. and Romheld, V.: Root excretion of carboxylic acids and protons in phosphorus-deficient plants. Plant Soil 211:121-130, 1999.

Ortiz-Monasterio, J. I., Manske, G. G. B. and Ginkel, van M.: Nitrigen and phosphorus use efficiency. In: Reynolds, M. P., Ortiz-Monasterio, J. I. and McNab, A. (eds), Application of physiology In wheat breeding. Mexico,D.F., CIMMYT, 200-207, 2001.

Ozturk, L., Eker, S., Torun, B. and Cakmak, I.: Variation in P efficiency among 73 bread and durum wheat genotypes grown in a P-deficient calcareous soil. Plant Soil 269: 69-80, 2005.

Paux, E., Sourdille, P., Mackay, I. and Feuillet, C.: Sequence-based marker development in wheat: Advances and applications to breeding. Biotechnol Adv Res Rev doi: 10.1016/j. biotecha dv, 2011.

Pereira, J. F., Zhou, G., Delhaize, E., Richardson, T., Zhou, M. and Ryan, P. R.: Engineering greater aluminium resistance in wheat by over-expressing *TaALMT1*. Ann Bot 106: 205–214, 2010.

Poirier, Y. and Bucher, M.: Phosphate transport and homeostasis in Arabidopsis. In: Somerville, C. R. and Meyerowitz, E. M. (eds), The Arabidopsis book. Rockville, MD: The American Society of Plant Biologists, 1–35, 2002.

Price, A. H.: Believe it or not, QTLs are accurate. Trends Plant Sci 11: 213–216, 2006.

Raboy, V.: Myo-inositol-1,2,3,4,5,6-hexakisphosphate. Phytochem 64: 1033–1043, 2003.

Raboy, V., Noaman, M. W., Taylor, G. A. and Pickett, S. G.: Grain phytic acid and protein are highly correlated in winter wheat. Crop Sci. 31: 631-635, 1991.

Raghothama, K. G.: Phosphate acquisition. Annu Rev Plant Physiol Plant Mol Biol50: 665–693, 1999.

Rebafka, F. P., Bationo, A. and Marschner, H.: Phosphorus seed coating increases phosphorus uptake, early growth and yield of pearl millet (*Pennisetumglaucum* (L.) R. Br.) grown on an acid sandy soil in Niger, West Africa. Ferti Res 35: 151-160, 1993.

Reisenauer, H. M.: Concentrations of nutrient ions in soil solution. In: Airman PH (ed) Environmental biology. Federation of American Societies for Experimental Biology, Bethesda, 507 - 508, 1966.

Richardson, A. E.: Prospects for using soil microorganisms to improve the acquisition of phosphorus by plants. Aust J Plant Physiol 28: 897–906, 2001.

Richardson, A. E., Barea, J. M., McNeill, A. M., Prigent-Combaret, C.: Acquisition of phosphorus and nitrogen in the rhizosphere and plant growth promotion by microorganisms. Plant Soil 321: 305–339, 2009.

Richardson, A. E. and Simpson, R. J.: Soil microorganisms mediating phosphorus availability. Plant Physiol 156: 989-996, 2011.

Sanchez, P. A.: Tripling crop yields in tropical Africa. Nat Geosci 3: 299–300, 2010.

Schulthess, U., Feil, B. and Jutzi, S. C.: Yield-independent variation in grain nitrogen and phosphorus concentration among Ethiopian wheats. Agron J 89: 497-506 , 1997.

Schweiger, P. and Jakobsen, I.: Direct measurement of phosphorus uptake by native arbuscularmycorrhizal fungi associated with field-grown winter wheat. Agron J 91: 998- 1002, 2000.

Seeling, B. and Jungk, A.: Utilization of organic phosphorus in calcium chloride extract of soil by barley plants and hydrolysis by acid and alkaline phosphatases. Plant Soil 178:179–184, 1996.

Sekiya, N. and Yano, K.: Seed P-enrichment as an effective P supply to wheat. Plant Soil 327: 347–354, 2010.

Singh, R., Behl, R. K., Moawad, A. K. and Gill, H.S.: Selection of wheat genotypes responsive to VA Mycorrhiza and *Azotobacter chroococcum*. In:Proceeding "The 6th International Symposium on Plant-Soil Interaction at low pH". August Sendai, Japan. 358-359, 2004.

Smith, F. W., Mudge, S. R., Rae, A.L. and Glassop, D.: Phosphate transport in plants. Plant Soil 248.71-83, 2003.

Smith, S. E., Dickson, S. and Smith, F. A.: Nutrient transfer in arbuscular mycorrhizas: how are fungal and plant processes integrated? Australian J Plant Physiol 28: 685–696, 2001.

Su, J. Y., Xiao, Y. M., Li, M., Liu, Q. Y., Li, B., Tong, Y. P., Jia, J. Z. and Li, Z.S.: Mapping QTLs for phosphorus-deficiency tolerance at wheat seedling stage. Plant Soil 281: 25–36, 2006.

Su, J. Y., Zheng, Q., Li, H. W., Li, B., Jing, R. L., Tong, Y. P. and Li, Z. S.: Detection of QTLs for phosphorus use efficiency in relation to agronomic performance of wheat grown under phosphorus sufficient and limited conditions. Plant Sci 176: 824–836, 2009.

Tabatabai, M. A. and Bremner, J. M.: Use of p-nitropheny1 phosphate for assay of soil phosphatase activity. Soil Bioi Biochem 1: 301-307, 1969.

Tittarelli, A., Milla, L., Vargas, F., Morales, A., Neupert, C., Meisel, L., Salvo, G. H., Penaloza, E., Munoz, G., Corcuera, L. and Silva, H.: Isolation and comparative analysis of the wheat *TaPT2* promoter: Identification *in silico* of new putative regulatory motifs conserved between monocots and dicots. J Exp Bot 58: 2573-2582, 2007.

Ullrich-Eberius, C. I., Novacky, A. and Bel, A. J. E.: Phosphate uptake in *Lemnagibba* GI: energetics and kinetics. Planta 161: 46–52, 1984.

Ullrich-Eberius, C. I., Novacky, A., Fisher, E. and Luttge, U.: Relationship between energy dependent phosphate uptake and the electrical membrane potential in *Lemnagibba* GI. Plant Physiol 67: 797–801, 1981.

Vance, C. P.: Symbiotic nitrogen fixation and phosphorus acquisition .Plant nutrition in a world of declining renewable resources. Plant Physiol 127: 390-397, 2001.

Vance, C. P.: Quantitative Trait Loci, Epigenetics, Sugars, and MicroRNAs: Quaternaries in Phosphate Acquisition and Use. Plant Physiol 154: 582–588, 2010.

Vance, C. P., Uhde-Stone, C. and Allan, D. L.: Phosphorus acquisition and use: critical adaptations by plants for securing a nonrenewable resource. New Phytol 157: 423–447, 2003.

Varshney, R. K., Langridge, P. and Graner, A.: Application of genomics to molecular breeding of wheat and barley. Adv Gen 58: 121–155, 2007.

Wang, L., Chen, F., Zhang, F. and Mi, G.: Two strategies for achieving higher yield under phosphorus deficiency in winter wheat grown in field conditions. Field Crops Res 118: 36–42, 2010.

Zeng, Y. J., Ying, J., Liu, J. Z., Sun, J. H., Li, B., Xiao, H. and Li, Z. S.: Function analysis of a wheat phosphate transporter in yeast mutant. Acta Genetica Sinica 29: 1017-1020, 2002.

Comparative Life Cycle Assessment of Flemish and Western Cape Pork Production

Laurens Devers[1], Theo Kleynhans[2]

[1]Master student in Tropical Natural Resources Management of the Katholieke Universiteit Leuven, Belgium;

[2]Prof. Theo Kleynhans, Department Agricultural Economics of the University of Stellenbosch and Prof. E. Mathijs, Head of the Division for Agricultural and Food Economics, Katholieke Universiteit Leuven, Belgium.

Abstract

Given the growing awareness of the impact of intensive livestock production and the transportation of feed and meat in the local and global environments, the common life cycle assessment (LCA) method was used to compare environmental impact scenarios involving producing pork in the Western Cape, and exporting it to Antwerp in Flanders versus producing pork in Flanders for the Belgian market, and also delivering it to Antwerp. In order to take into account many different environmental impacts, the complete pig production chain (a cradle-to-gate life cycle) was covered by the LCAs done on the Western Cape and Flemish case studies. An additional pork shipping activity was added in the case of the Western Cape pork chain. In all impact categories, the Western Cape Province scores lower than Flanders when a FU of one kg of pork meat is used as the basis of comparison, signalling environmentally less friendly pork production in the Western Cape. The feed provision activity has been shown to have the largest impact on energy use and GWP, while manure has the largest impact on eutrophication and acidification potential. Furthermore, one kg of pork is more expensive in the Western Cape than in Flanders.

Introduction

Given the growing awareness of the impact of intensive livestock production and the transportation of feed and meat in the local and global environments, the common life cycle assessment (LCA) method was used to compare environmental impact scenarios involving producing pork in the Western Cape, and exporting it to Antwerp in Flanders versus producing pork in Flanders for the Belgian market, and also delivering it to Antwerp. It was expected that the energy needed for heating pig houses in the Western Cape and for transporting the pork to the Flemish export market, together with the associated emissions, would be lower than the energy needed and resultant emissions to produce pork in the colder Flemish climate. If this could be proven, the South African Pork Producers' Organisation (SAPPO) could use this information to start developing an image of South African pork in the export markets as being produced in an environmentally friendly manner. SAPPO (2009) describes the South African pork industry as *"while small, a dynamic, well-organised agricultural industry that compares favourably with the rest of the world in terms of production outputs"*.

17

Material and Methods

Life cycle assessment (LCA) is a methodology that takes into account all the environmental effects of the entire life cycle of a product: the extraction of raw materials, manufacturing, distribution, transportation, maintenance, recycling, emissions and final disposal (Wegener Sleeswijk et al., 1996). LCA emerged in the early 1970s to assess the material flows, energy efficiency, and raw material consumption and to some extent the waste disposal of industrial companies. As LCA applications were often disappointing and led to false conclusions, ISO norms were set up to create some firm rules for its use (Jensen et al., 1997). The LCA methodology is described in international standards ISO 14040-14043 (ISO 14040, 1997; ISO 14041, 1998; ISO 14042, 1998; ISO 14043, 1998). Life cycle thinking is currently one of the five key principles in the European Union's Integrated Product Policy.

In order to take into account many different environmental impacts, the complete pig production chain (a cradle-to-gate life cycle) was covered by the LCAs done on the Western Cape and Flemish case studies, including (i) the feed provision activity, which included the production of raw materials and feed, (ii) the pig farming activity, (iii) the slaughter house activity and (iv) the slurry (treatment) activity. An additional (v) pork shipping activity was added in the case of the Western Cape pork chain.

The functional unit (FU) is the functional output of a product, to which the assessed environmental impacts are scaled (ISO 14040, 1997). The functional unit used in this study is defined as one kg of Western Cape or Flemish pork (carcass weight) delivered to a distribution centre in Antwerp. Carcass weight is chosen because the ratio of live weight to carcass weight differs between the two regions. The computer program used in this study for calculating impacts was the GaBi 4 program.

In Flanders, official confidentiality restrictions excluded access to the data of any particular pig farm. A model of a typical 223-sow unit was therefore constructed from data available in different databases and from coordinating institutes. As such databases do not exist in South Africa, a specific 700-sow unit as a fairly typical pig farm in the Western Cape was chosen as a case study. Both are closed piggeries where the piglets and weaners are raised as well as fattened.

The following environmental impact categories were included in this study:

- Global warming potential (GWP): climate change
- This reflects an increase in temperature due to emissions of greenhouse gasses (GHG) like carbon dioxide (CO_2), methane (CH_4) and nitrous oxide (N_2O). The results are expressed in kg CO_2 equivalents calculated over a time horizon of 100 years.
- Eutrophication potential
- The leaching, runoff, and volatilisation of increased concentrations of nitrates and phosphates into nearby ecosystems are generally the biggest contributors to eutrophication potential (Vezjak et al., 1998). The results are characterised in kg PO_4 equivalents.
- Acidification potential

- A sensitive (im-)balance between ecosystems' internal and external H^+ sources, and internal H^+ sinks of different capacities and reaction rates is the main cause of acidification (Lükewille and Alewell, 2008). The release of acidic gasses like SO_2, NO_x and NH_3 has the most potential to react with water in the atmosphere and form acids like H_2SO_4 and HNO_3. The results are expressed in kg SO_2 equivalents.

- Energy use

- Establishing the total energy use of the pork chain is a way of measuring its efficiency in using renewable and non-renewable power. The results are expressed in MJ equivalents (Wegener Sleeswijk et al., 1996).

The computer program used in this study for calculating impacts was the GaBi 4 program. This software is maintained by PE International. The program translates inputs and outputs into environmental impacts in different impact categories. For this study, the incorporated "GaBi 2006" database was used. It is the most comprehensive, up-to-date life cycle inventory database available (GaBi, 2009).

Results

Figure 1 shows total *Global Warming Potential (GWP)* values of 2.55 kg CO_2-eq (FU)-1 for the Flemish pork chain and 4.5 kg CO_2-eq (FU)-1 for the Western Cape chain. The absolute difference in GWP between the Western Cape and Flanders is greatest for the feed provision activity (0.68 kg CO_2-eq (FU)-1), second for the slaughterhouse activity (0.53 kg CO_2-eq (FU)-1), third the pig farming activity (0.34 kg CO_2-eq (FU)-1), fourth for the pig slurry treatment activity (0.23 kg CO_2-eq (FU)-1) and last for the pork shipping activity (0.16 kg CO_2-eq (FU)-1). Pork shipping only occurs from the Western Cape to Flanders.

In the Western Cape, more than 60 percent of pig feed is comprised of maize, while in Flanders, this ingredient represents only 7 percent, with wheat and wheat co-products making up 50 percent of Flemish pig feed. In the case of the Western Cape, maize has to be transported some 1,200 km to the feed factory. Increasing the use of locally produced main feed ingredients can reduce impacts for all categories.

The main reason for the difference in GWP of the slaughterhouse activity lies in differences in diesel composition and the higher electricity use – 1.66 MJ $(FU)^{-1}$ for the Western Cape compared with 0.28 MJ $(FU)^{-1}$ for Flanders. This, added to the higher impact of electricity per MJ in the Western Cape due to the use of coal, gives a GWP ten times higher for the Western Cape than for Flanders. In addition, gas combustion plays a role in the higher GWP of the Western Cape slaughterhouse.

Electricity is also the key GWP determinant for the pig farming activity. Electricity used at pig farms in Western Cape is almost double that used in Flanders, the main reason for this difference being that in the Western Cape, the weaners are heated by heat bulbs. Central heating, more specifically floor heating, is used in Flanders.

The emissions caused by the slurry and the slurry treatment activity are more or less the same for the Western Cape and for Flanders. Factors influencing the GWP of this activity are (i) the feed conversion ratio (2.97 for Flanders and 3.45 for the Western Cape), (ii) the live weight at slaughter (112.5 kg for Flanders and 90-100 kg for the Western Cape), (iii) the difference in feed composition influencing emissions and (iv) the slurry treatment. The added impact of the first two factors results in the Western Cape producing 14.28 kg of slurry (FU)-1 compared with the 14.01 kg of slurry (FU)-1 produced in Flanders. Attention needs to be paid to new techniques like anaerobic digestion, since they show promising results for reducing the impacts of generating pig slurry and treating it in South Africa.

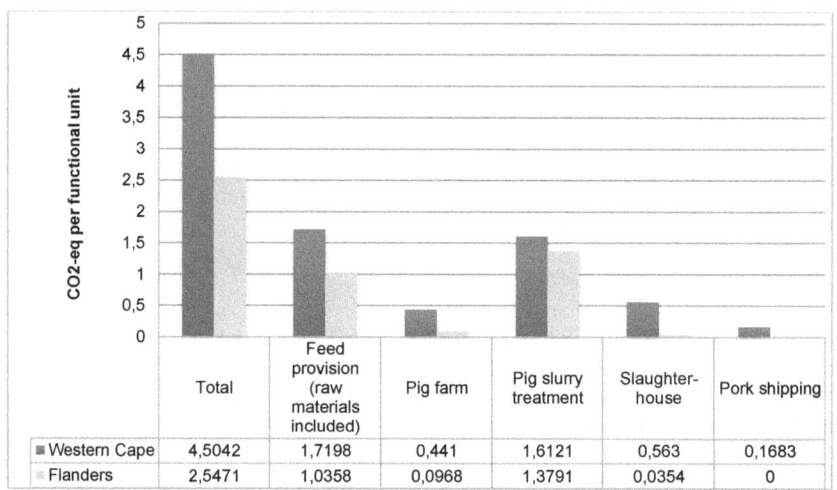

	Total	Feed provision (raw materials included)	Pig farm	Pig slurry treatment	Slaughter-house	Pork shipping
■ Western Cape	4,5042	1,7198	0,441	1,6121	0,563	0,1683
Flanders	2,5471	1,0358	0,0968	1,3791	0,0354	0

Figure 1: GWP for different pork chain activities in Western Cape and Flanders (kg CO_2 equivalent)

The total *eutrophication potential* of the Flemish pork production chain is 0.022 kg PO_4-eq $(FU)^{-1}$. For the Western Cape it is 0.034 kg PO_4-eq $(FU)^{-1}$, 50% more than that of Flanders (see Figure 2). The main contributor to eutrophication is leaching of N and phosphate from pig excretions, and to a lesser extent, ammonia emissions to the atmosphere. The eutrophication impact of pig slurry treatment is 0.0078 kg PO_4-eq $(FU)^{-1}$ more in the Western Cape, and for the feed provision activity, it is 0.0023 kg PO_4-eq $(FU)^{-1}$ more in the Western Cape than in Flanders. The high impact of eutrophication potential in the Western Cape feed provision activity relative to that of Flanders, is mainly caused by the maize component of Western Cape pig feed. Maize contributes almost half of the eutrophication potential of the Western Cape. The eutrophication impact of the slaughterhouse-, pig farm- and pork shipping activities are negligible. Diet and the pig slurry treatment methods have a larger influence on eutrophication potential than on GWP. Dalgaard et al. (2007) argue that digestibility of the feed has large impacts on eutrophication potential.

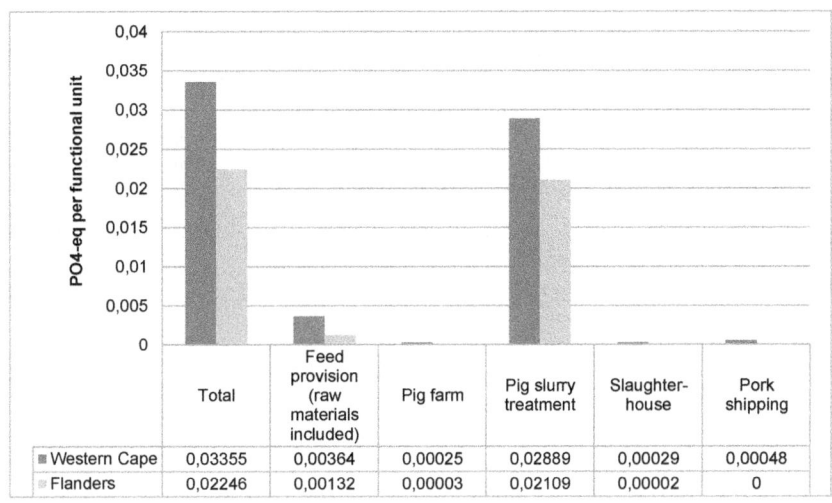

Figure 2: Eutrophication potential for different pork chain activities in Western Cape and Flanders (kg PO$_4$ –equivalent)

The total contributions of *acidification potential* in the Flemish and Western Cape pork production chains are 0.039 kg SO$_2$-eq (FU)-1 and 0.063 kg SO$_2$-eq (FU)-1 respectively (see Figure 3).

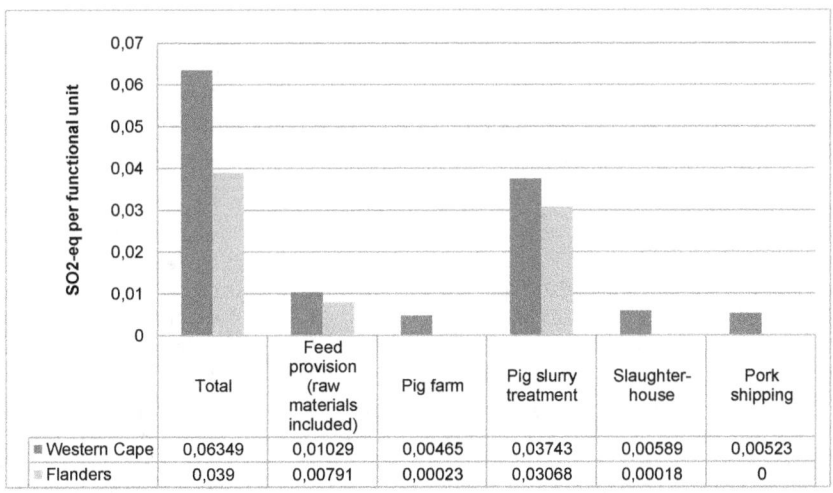

Figure 3: Acidification potential for different pork chain activities in Western Cape and Flanders (kg PO$_4$-equivalent)

The absolute difference in total acidification potential between the Western Cape and Flanders is greatest for the pig slurry treatment activity (0.0067 kg SO_2-eq $(FU)^{-1}$), followed by the slaughterhouse activity, the pork shipping activity, the pig farming activity and the feed provision activity (0.0057, 0.0052, 0.0043 and 0.0024 kg SO_2-eq $(FU)^{-1}$ respectively). The differences in acidification potential in the slaughterhouse and pig farming activity between the Western Cape and Flanders can be explained in terms of the much higher electricity use of the Western Cape.

Total *energy use* for the pork production chain is 18.3 MJ (FU)-1 in Flanders and 30.7 MJ (FU)-1 in the Western Cape (see Figure 4).

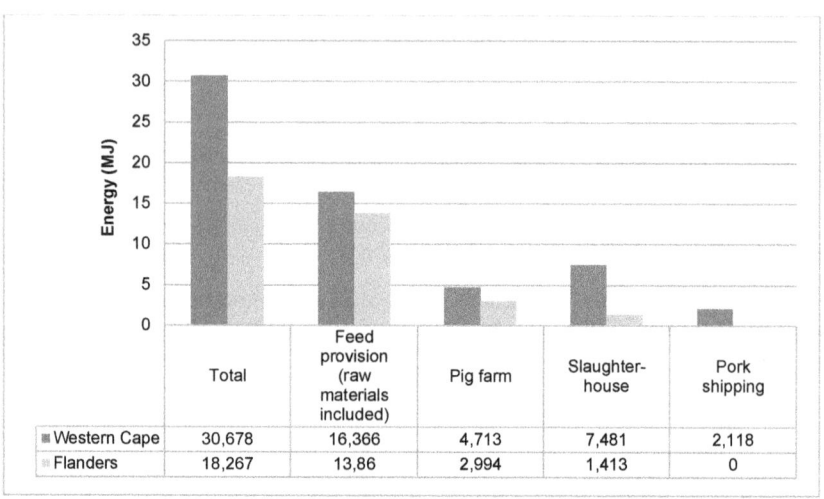

	Total	Feed provision (raw materials included)	Pig farm	Slaughter-house	Pork shipping
Western Cape	30,678	16,366	4,713	7,481	2,118
Flanders	18,267	13,86	2,994	1,413	0

Figure 4: Energy use for different pork chain activities in Western Cape and Flanders (MJ per functional unit)

The absolute difference in total energy use between the Western Cape and Flanders is greatest for the slaughterhouse activity (6.07 MJ (FU)-1), second for the feed provision activity (2.5 MJ (FU)-1), third the pork shipping activity (2.1 MJ (FU)-1), and last for the pig farming activity (1.72 MJ (FU)-1). The energy use of the slurry treatment activity is included in the energy use of the pig farming activity, since the energy for separating the slurry comes from the pig farm; also, trucks exporting the slurry are incorporated in the pig farming activity.

The significant difference in the impacts of electricity use between the two regions is due to the higher electricity usage per functional unit in Western Cape, and the different sources of power in the regions. In Flanders electricity is generated mainly by nuclear power, while in South Africa it is generated mainly by coal combustion (Consult the GaBi 2006 database for details).

Conclusions

The identification and quantification of the main environmental impacts of the pork life cycle chain revealed the contributions of the various pork production activities to the various impact categories. The feed provision activity, which includes the cultivation and production of raw materials, has been shown to have the largest impact on energy use and GWP, while manure (treatment) has the largest impact on eutrophication and acidification potential.

In all impact categories, the Western Cape province of South Africa scores lower than Flanders when a FU of one kg of pork meat is used as the basis of comparison, signalling environmentally less friendly pork production in the Western Cape. Furthermore, one kg of pork is more expensive in the Western Cape than in Flanders. The price per FU on leaving the slaughterhouse in Flanders is Euro 1.55 (ZAR 13.95), while in the Western Cape, it is Euro 1.805 (ZAR 16.245) per FU (ZAR 9 = 1 Euro).

The choice of one kg of pork as the functional unit in this study favours the Flemish pork chain. If the eutrophication and acidification potentials were measured in terms of an area unit, the outcome would be more favourable for the Western Cape, as this region is in a far better position to accommodate the local impact of pig slurry than Flanders.

Acknowledgements

The authors wish to thank SAPPO (the South African Pork Producers' Organisation) for the financial support for this study and for providing access to the data, specifically to Mr. Stefan Guizot and Mr. Mike Herambs for providing data on a typical Western Cape pig farm; and to Mr. Toon De Keukelaere of Boerenbond Vlaanderen, who supported the collection of data on the average Flemish pig farm.

References

Dalgaard, R. : *The environmental impact of pork production from a life cycle perspective*. Ph.D. Dissertation. Tjele, Denmark: Department of agro ecology and environment, Aarhus University, 2007.

GaBi: *Handbook for Life Cycle Assessment (LCA). Using the GaBi Education software package*. PE International. [Online]. www.pe- international.com (Accessed 16/08/2010), 2009.

GaBi database:. PE International GmbH and University of Stuttgart (former IKP). [Online]. http://www.gabi-software.com (Accessed 18/08/2010), 2006.

ISO (International Organisation for Standardization): ISO 14040. Environmental management life cycle assessment: principles and framework. Geneva: International Standard, 1997.

ISO (International Organisation for Standardization): ISO 14041. Environmental management-life cycle assessment: principles and framework. Geneva: International Standard, 1998.

ISO (International Organisation for Standardization): ISO 14042. Environmental management-life cycle assessment: principles and framework. Geneva: International Standard, 1998.

ISO (International Organisation for Standardization): ISO 14043. Environmental management-life cycle assessment: principles and framework. Geneva: International Standard, 1998.

Jensen, A., Hoffman, L., Moller, B. T., Schmidt, A., Christiansen, K., Elkington, J. and Van Dijk: Life Cycle Assessment: A guide to approaches, experiences and information sources. European environment agency. Copenhagen, Denmark, 119, 1997.

Lükewille, A. and Alewell, C.: *Acidification*. Encyclopedia of Ecology. Academic Press, Oxford, UK. ISBN 978-0-08-045405-4, 2008.

SAPPO (South African Pork Producers, Organisation): *The South African Pork Industry, the big picture*. SAPPO information leaflet, 2009.

Vezjak, M., Savsek, T. and Stuhler, E. A.: System dynamics of eutrophication processes in lakes. *European Journal of Operational Research* 109: 442-451, 1998.

Wegener Sleeswijk, A., Kleijn, R., Van Zeijts, H., Reus, JAWA., Meeuwsen–van Onna, MIG., Leneman, H. and Sengers, HHWJM.: Application of LCA to agricultural products. Leiden: CML (Centre of Environmental Science) Leiden University, 1996.

Contributions of Plant and Animal Breeders for Sustainable Agriculture

Gerhard Flachowsky,

Institute of Animal Nutrition, Friedrich-Loeffler-Institute (FLI), Federal Research Institute for Animal Health, Bundesallee 50, 38116 Braunschweig, Germany

Abstract

The world population is still growing up and asking for more and better food. Sustainability in feed and food production is a key challenge for agriculture. In the future there will be a strong competition for arable land and further limited resources such as fossil carbon-sources, water, and some minerals between feed/food, fuel, fibre, areas for settlements and natural protected areas. There is no essential need for food of animal origin, but the consumption of meat, fish, milk and eggs may contribute significantly to meet the human requirements in amino acids and some important trace nutrients. About one third of the daily protein intake should consist of protein of animal origin. In addition feed/food production causes emissions with a certain greenhouse gas potential such as carbon dioxide from fossil fuel, methane from the enteric fermentation esp. in ruminants and from the excrement management as well as nitrogen compounds from the protein metabolism in the animals.

Plant and animal breeding are the starting points of sustainable land use and the food chain. High and stable yields of low input varieties should be the main aims of plant breeding. The conversion of feed into food of animal origin is associated with high energy and nutrient losses and emissions in the environment. Animal breeders may substantially contribute to a more efficient conversion of feed. Challenges for plant and animal breeders are demonstrated and discussed in the paper.

Introduction

The world population is still growing up and asking for more and better food. In October 2011 the 7th billions people will be born. Sustainability in feed and food production is a key challenge for agriculture. In the future there will be a strong competition for arable land and further limited resources such as fossil carbon-sources, water, some minerals (such as phosphorus) between feed/food, fuel, fibre, areas for settlements and natural protected areas. According to FAO (2009) the human population will globally increase from currently about 7 to 9 billion people in 2050, but the estimated need for meat and milk will nearly double during this time (Steinfeld et al. 2006).

There is no essential need for food of animal origin, but the consumption of meat, fish, milk and eggs may contribute significantly to meet the human requirements in amino acids and some important trace nutrients (such as Ca, P, Zn, Mn, Fe, I, Se, Vitamins A, D, E, some B-vitamins) esp. for children as well as for pregnant and lactating women. Human nutritionists (e.g. Jackson, 2007; Waterlow, 1999) recommend that about one third of the daily protein demand (0.75 – 1 g per kg body weight) should originate from protein of animal origin. That corresponds to about 20 g of the daily intake of 60 g should be based on protein of animal origin, which is higher than the present average consumption (23.9 g per day; Table 1).

Table 1: Intake of milk, meat and eggs as well protein of animal origin per inhabitant and year (min and max-values, global averages and Germany for comparison; kg per inhabitant and year: data from 2005)

Food	Minimum	Average	Maximum	Germany
Milk	1.3 (PR Kongo)	82.1	367.7 (Sweden)	248.7
Meat[1]	3.1 (Bangla-desh)	41.2	126.6 (USA)	83.3
Eggs	0.1 (PR Kongo)	9.0	20.2 (PR China)	11.8
Edible protein of animal origin (g per human and day)	1.7 (Burundi)	23.9	69.0 (USA)	52.8
Portion of animal protein in % of total protein intake per person	4.0 (Burundi)	27.9	59.5 (USA)	53.7

[1] Probably empty body weight (meat plus bones)   Source: FAO, 2009

On the other side there is a high variation in availability and consumption of food of animal origin between persons and countries (between 1.7 and above 60 g protein of animal origin per person and day; see Table 1). Another reason for foods of animal origin is the generally high bioavailability of the nutrients and their considerable enjoyment value. Such food is also considered as an indicator for the standard of living in many regions of the world. Other reasons for the higher demand of food of animal origin in some countries are the increased income of the population (Keyzer et al., 2005) and the imitation of the so-called Western style of life (nutrition).

In addition, feed/food production causes emissions with a certain greenhouse gas potential such as carbon dioxide (CO_2) from fossil fuel, methane (CH_4) from the enteric fermentation esp. in ruminants and from the excrement management as well as nitrogen compounds (NH_3; N_2O) from the protein metabolism in the animals (see DEFRA, 2006; FAO, 2010; Grünberg et al., 2010; Leip et al., 2010; Flachowsky et al., 2011; see Table 2). Apart from the low input of limited resources along the food chain a low output of minerals such as phosphorus and some trace elements and greenhouse gases (CO_2, CH_4 and N_2O) during feed/food production are very important aims of sustainable agriculture.

Table 2: Effects of animal species, categories and performances on some emissions (per kg edible protein)

Protein source (Body weight)	Performance per day	N-excretion (% of intake)	Methane emission (g per day)[3]	Emissions in kg per kg Protein			
				P	N	CH$_4$[3]	CO$_{2eq}$[4]
Dairy cow (650kg)	10kg milk	75	310	0.10	0.65	1.0	30
	20kg milk	70	380	0.06	0.44	0.6	16
	40kg milk	65	520	0.04	0.24	0.4	12
Dairy goat (60kg)	2kg milk	75	50	0.08	0.5	0.8	20
	5kg milk	65	60	0.04	0.2	0.4	10
Beef cattle (350kg)	500g[1]	90	170	0.30	2.3	3.5	110
	1000g[1]	84	175	0.18	1.3	1.7	55
	1500g[1]	80	180	0.14	1.0	1.2	35
Grow-ing/fattening pig (80kg)	500g[1]	85	5	0.20	1.0	0.12	16
	700g[1]	80	5	0.12	0.7	0.08	12
	900g[1]	75	5	0.09	0.55	0.05	10
Broilers (1.5kg)	40g[1]	70	Traces	0.04	0.35	0.01	4
	60g[1]	60		0.03	0.25	0.01	3
Laying hen (1.8kg)	50%[2]	80	Traces	0.12	0.6	0.03	7
	70%[2]	65		0.07	0.4	0.02	5
	90%[2]	55		0.05	0.3	0.02	3

[1]Daily weight gain [2]Laying performance [3]CH$_4$-emission depending on composition of diet [4]Adequate to Carbon Footprints (sum of greenhouse gas emission of CO$_2$; CH$_4$ (x 23) and N$_2$0 (x 300; IPCC 2006) for edible protein of animal origin
Source: Flachowsky, 2002, 2011)

Challenges for Plant Breeding

Plant breeding and cultivation are the key elements and starting points for feed and food security during the next years (see Flachowsky, 2008, SCAR, 2008, The Royal Society, 2009). The most important objectives for plant breeders can be summarized as follows:

- High yields with low external inputs (low input varieties) such as water, minerals, fossil fuel, plant protection substances etc.
- Efficient use of natural unlimited resources such as sun energy, nitrogen and carbon dioxide in the air
- Optimise the genetic potential of plants for a highly efficient photosynthesis

- Lower concentrations of toxic substances such as secondary plant ingredients, myco-toxins from toxin-producing fungi, toxins from anthropogenic activities or geogenic origin
- Lower concentrations of substances that influence the use or bioavailability of nutrients such as lignin, phytate, enzyme inhibitors, tannins etc.
- Higher concentrations of the nutritive value determining components such as nutrient precursors, nutrients, enzymes, prebiotics, essential oils etc.

From the global view of feed and food security low input varieties have the highest priority. Furthermore, often undesirable substances cannot be removed from feedstuffs, or can only be removed with great effort (Verstrate, 2011). Therefore the decrease of undesirable substances in plants is also an important objective of plant breeding. From the perspective of nutrition, an increase of essential nutrients (e.g. amino acids, fatty acids, trace elements, vitamins etc.) could be very favourable in some regions of the world to meet the requirements of man and animal with essential nutrients. But this aspect is not so important in parts of the world like Europe because of the availability of a large amount of food and feed additives on the market.

It is possible to fulfil the objectives of plant breeding mentioned above by conventional breeding (Flachowsky, 2012). But in the future methods of biotechnology may be more flexible, more potent and faster. "New" plants, newly expressed proteins in plants and/or changed composition of plants are real challenges for animal and human nutritionists for safety and nutritional assessment of such products.

Increasing feed/food demands require higher plant yields and/or more area for production. Because of some limited resources, low input plants are an important prerequisite to solving future problems and to establishing a sustainable agriculture. Such plants should be very efficient in the use of mineral plant nutrients (incl. N), fuel, water and arable land (high yields), but they should also be able to very effectively use sun energy and unlimited plant nutrients from the air (such as N_2 and CO_2; see Table 3). Furthermore the genetic pool available in plants, animals and microorganisms should contribute to optimize plants and animals for a more efficient conversion of limited resources into feed and food.

Table 3: Potentials to produce phytogenic biomass and their availability per inhabitant under consideration of the increase of population ($\uparrow$ Increase, $\downarrow$ Decrease, $\leftrightarrow$ no important influence)

Plant nutrients in the atmosphere (N_2, CO_2)	$\uparrow \leftrightarrow$
Sun energy	$\leftrightarrow$
Agricultural area	$\downarrow$
Water	$\downarrow$
Fossil Energy	$\downarrow$
Mineral plant nutrients	$\downarrow$
Variation of genetic pool	$\uparrow$

Source: Flachowsky, 2010

Challenges for Animal Breeding

The global number of livestock animals used in agricultural production has been estimated to be 1.8 billion large ruminants, incl. cattle, buffaloes and camels, 2.4 billion small ruminants (sheep and goats), nearly 1 billion pigs, and about 20 billion of poultry.

Conversion of feed into food of animal origin is associated with energy and nutrient losses and environmental pollution, including excretion of Nitrogen (N), Phosphorus (P), trace elements, Carbon dioxide (CO_2), Methane (CH_4) etc. (see Table 2). The resources such as fuel, water, arable land and specific minerals such as P are limited (see Table 3), but needed for synthesis of phytogenic biomass as fodder for animals (Flachowsky, 2008). Only a small proportion of feed is converted into food products by the animals. This amount is variable and depends on animal species, the performance of the individual animal and several other factors. Most of the substances are emitted into the environment (Table 2).

The main purpose for maintaining farm animals in such great quantities is the production of valuable protein for human consumption. Large differences exist in protein yields per animal or per kg body weight depending on species and production category as well as performance status (see Table 2). Based on the predicted meat and milk production in 2050 (Steinfeld et al., 2006), an average of 32 g edible protein of animal origin per men and day would be available.

Approximately, one third of the global greenhouse gas emission stems from agricultural production (Isermeyer et al., 2008). Ruminants contribute substantially to global methane emission (Kebreab et al., 2006; Flachowsky and Brade, 2007; Jouany, 2008). Carbon Footprints (CO_{2eq}) are indicative for CO_2-emission (e.g. per kg of milk or meat; see Table 2) and should alert producers and consumers of animal products for the environmental issues. Carbon Footprints per product serve as important parameter for determining the efficiency of food production. FAO (2010) has calculated Carbon Footprints on a global scale and found values between 1.3 kg $CO_{2eq.}$ per kg milk in North America and Europe and 7.5 kg $CO_{2eq.}$ per kg milk in sub-Saharan Africa. Selected emissions with their corresponding CO_2-footprints per kg edible protein are shown in Table 2. To reduce greenhouse gas emission of the global animal population, the ratio of production/consumption of feed of animal origin has to be reduced and the production of phytogenic biomass has to be increased. The overall efficiency of feed conversion into animal derived food for human consumption has to be improved.

Strategies to produce animals with better utilization of feed into animal derived food while concomitantly decreasing emission per product include:

- Higher feed intake of animals to improve the ratio between energy/nutrient requirements for maintenance and animal yields (Table 4);

- Higher digestibility of feed to make energy/nutrients more available from the same feed amount

- Reduction of energy losses in the digestive tract (e.g. CH_4, Table 5);

- Higher absorption of the digested nutrients

- Lower energy/nutrient requirements for maintenance of the animals (Tables 6);

- Lower energy need for protein synthesis in the body or increase of anabolic processes and lower catabolic processes in the animal

- Lower fat content in animal bodies or lower excretion of fat in milk and eggs or lower excretion of lactose in milk (lower energy content in products)

- Improved animal health, specifically animals with higher resistance against biotic and/or abiotic stressors and lower losses during production may also contribute to a more efficient conversion of feed.

Table 4: Model calculation to show the influence of dry matter intake (DMI; 7.0 MJ NEL/kg DM) of dairy cows (body weight: 650 kg; 4% milk fat; GfE 2001) on energy intake, percentage of maintenance, milk yield, energy per kg of milk as well as emissions per kg of milk.

Dry Matter Intake (DMI, kg per day)	10	15	20	25	30
Energy intake (MJ NEL per day)	70	105	140	175	210
Maintenance (37.7 MJ NEL per cow per day; % of total NEL-Intake)	53.9	35.9	26.9	21.5	18.0
Milk yield (3.3 MJ NEL per kg)	9.8	20.4	31.0	41.6	52.2
Net energy per kg milk (MJ NEL per kg milk)	7.1	5.1	4.5	4.2	4.0
Methane emission[1] (g per day)	240	360	480	600	720
(g per kg milk)	24.5	17.6	15.5	14.4	13.8
Carbon footprint (g CO_{2eq} per kg milk)[2]	825	605	530	495	475

[1] According to Flachowsky and Brade, 2007: 24g CH_4 per kg DMI for all diets
[2] Calculated on the base of the greenhouse potential of CH_4 (x 23) and the calculations by Daemmgen and Haenel, 2008
Source: Niemann, et al., 2011

Table 5: Model calculation to show the influence of methane reduction on the energy available for dairy cows and milk yields (Conditions for calculation: DMI: 20 kg per cow per day; Body weight: 650 kg per cow, 7 MJ NEL per kg DM with 20 g CH_4-emission)

Methane reduction (g per kg DMI) (g per cow per day)	30 / 600	25 / 500	20 / 400	15 / 300
Energy intake (MJ NEL per day)	130	135	140	145
Milk yield (kg per day)	28.0	29.5	31.0	32.5
Methane emission (g per kg milk)	21.4	17.0	12.9	9.2
Carbon footprint (g CO_{2eq} per kg milk)	735	585	440	315

Source: Niemann, et al., 2011

Table 6: Model calculation to show the influence of various energy maintenance require-ments on milk yield of lactating cows (Body weight: 650 kg per cow, DMI: 20 kg per day; Net energy content of feed: 7.0 MJ NEL per kg DM)

Maintenance requirements for energy (MJ NEL per kg BW$^{0.75}$) (MJ NEL per cow per day)	0.2 25.7	0.25 32.2	0.3 38.6	0.35 45.0	0.40 51.5
Energy intake (MJ NEL per cow per day)	140	140	140	140	140
Maintenance in % of NEL-intake	18.4	23.0	27.6	32.1	36.8
Milk yield (kg per cow per day)	34.6	32.7	30.7	28.8	26.8
Methane emission (g per cow per day) (g per kg milk)	480 13.9	480 14.7	480 15.6	480 16.7	480 17.9
Carbon footprints (g CO$_{2eq}$ per kg milk)	480	505	535	575	615

Source: Niemann, et al., 2011

Animal nutrition between plant and animal breeding

Animal nutrition has to contribute and to act as an important element in the food chain between plant breeding and plant production on one side and animal breeding and animal husbandry on the other side (Figure 1). In this function animal nutritionists may substantial contribute to a sustainable production of food of animal origin.

Figure 1: Animal nutrition (nutritional assessment of feeds) between plant and animal breeding

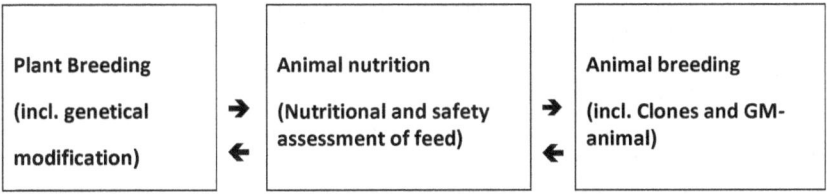

| Plant Breeding (incl. genetical modification) | → ← | Animal nutrition (Nutritional and safety assessment of feed) | → ← | Animal breeding (incl. Clones and GM-animal) |

Conclusions

Plant and animal breeding are the starting points of sustainable land use and the food chain. High and stable yields of low input varieties should be the main aims of plant breed-ing. The conversion of feed into food of animal origin is associated with high energy and nu-trient losses and emissions in the environment. Animal breeders may substantially contrib-ute to a more efficient conversion of feed.

References

Daemmgen, U. and Haenel, H.-D.: Emissions of greenhouse gases and gaseous air pollutants – a challenge for animal nutrition. Proc. Soc. Nutr. Physiol. 17, 163-167, 2008.

DEFRA: Determination the environmental burdens and resource use in the production of agriculture and horticulture commodities. Defra project report 2005, Cranfield, Univ. Silsoe Inst. http://www.cranfield.ac.uk, 2006.

FAO: The state of food and agriculture – Livestock in the balance. Rome, 180 p. 2009.

FAO: Greenhouse gas emissions from the dairy sector. A Life Cycle Assessment, Rome 94 p. 2010.

Flachowsky, G.: Efficiency of energy and nutrient use in the production of edible protein of animal origin. J. Appl. Anim. Res. 22:1-24, 2002.

Flachowsky, G.: What do animal nutritionists expect from plant breeding? Outlook on Agricult. 37: 95-103, 2008.

Flachowsky, G.: Global food security: Is there any solution? (in German), NovoArgumente 105-3-4, 2010, 64-68, 2010.

Flachowsky, G.: Carbon-footprints for food of animal origin, reduction potentials and research need. J. Appl. Anim. Res. 39, 2-14, 2011.

Flachowsky, G.: Prospects of feed from genetically modified plants in Livestock feeding. In: Animal Nutrition – Advances and Developments by U.R. Mehra, P. Singh, A.K. Verma (Eds.); Satish Serial Publishing House, Azadpur, Dehli (India), 475-498, 2012.

Flachowsky, G. and Brade, W.: Potentiale zur Reduzierung der Methan-Emissionen bei Wiederkäuern. Züchtungskunde 79, 417-465, 2007.

Flachowsky, G., Brade, W., Feil, A., Kamphues, J., Meyer and U., Zehetmeyer, M.: Carbon (CO_2)-footprints for producing food of animal origin – Data base and reduction potentials. Übersichten zur Tierernährung 39, 1-45, 2011.

Flachowsky, G. and Hachenberg, S.: CO_2-Footprints for food of animal origin – Present stage and open questions. J. Consumer Prot. Food Safety 4, 190-198, 2009.

Grünberg, J., Nieberg, H. und Schmidt, T.: Treibhausgasbilanzierung von Lebensmitteln (Carbon Footprints): Überblick und kritische Reflektion. Landbauforschung – vTI Agriculture and Forestry Research 60, 53-72, 2010.

IPCC (Intergovernmental Panel on Climate Change): IPCC Guidelines for National Greenhouse Gas Inventories, IPCC, Bracknell, UK, 2006.

Jackson, A. A.: Protein. – In: Mann. J. and S. Truswell (eds.): Essentials in human nutrition. Oxford Univ. Press (3rd ed.), 53-72, 2008.

Jouany, J.-P.: Enteric methane production by ruminants and its control. In: Gut efficiency; the key ingredients in ruminants. Ed. by A. Andrieu and D. Wilde, Wageningen Academic Publ., 35-59, 2008.

Kebreab, E., Johnson, K. A., Archibeque, S. I., Pape, D. and Wirtgh, T.: Model for estimating enteric methane emissions from the United States dairy and feedlot cattle. J. Anim. Sci. 86, 2738-2748, 2008.

Keyzer, M. A., Merbis, M. D., Pavel, L. F. P. W. and van Westenbeck, C. F. A.: Diets shifts towards meat and the effect on cereal use: Can we feed the animals in 2030? Ecological Economics 55: 187-202, 2005.

Leip, A., Weiss, F., Monni, S., Perez, I., Fellmann, T., Loudjami, P., Tuiello, F., Grandgirard, D., Monni, S. and Biala, K.: Evaluation of the livestock sector's contribution to the EU greenhouse gas emissions (GGELS) – Final report, JRC, EU, 2010.

Niemann, H., Kuhla, B. and Flachowsky, G.: The perspectives for feed efficient animal production. Online before print, June 24, 2011, doi: 10.2527/jas 2011-4236 J. ANIM Sci., 2011.

SCAR (EU Commission – Standing Committee on Agricultural Research): New challenges for agricultural research. Climate change, rural development, agricultural knowledge systems, The 2nd SCAR Foresight Exercise, Brussels, Dec. 2008, 112 p., 2008.

Steinfeld, H., Gerber, P., Wassenaar, T., Castel, V., Rosales, M. and de Haan, C.: Livestock's long shadow: Environmental issues and options, FAO, Rome, 2006.

The Royal Society: Reaping the benefits: Science and the sustainable intensification of global agriculture, RS policy document 11/09, issued Oct. 2009 RS 1608, ISBN: 978-0-85403-784-1, 2009.

Verstrate, F.: Risk management of undesirable substances in feed following updated risk assessments. Toxicology and Applied Pharmacology, available Online, 2011.

Waterlow, J. C.: The mysteries of nitrogen balance. Nutr. Res. Rev. 12, 25-54, 1999.

Less Work – More Rice?

Gender Equality through New Systems of Rice Cultivation in Timor-Leste

Karoline Hemminger

Msc Student Sustainable International Agriculture, Georg-August-University of Göttingen and Kassel University
karoline.hemminger@web.de. This paper summarizes the results of a bachelor thesis in agricultural sciences at the Humboldt- University Berlin. Supervisors: Dr. Parto Teherani-Krönner, Prof. Matthias Weiter

Abstract:

The purpose of this study was to find the effects of the introduction of the new system of rice cultivation ICM (Integrated Crop Management) on gender arrangements of rural households in Timor-Leste. Qualitative research was conducted during a three month placement in the GIZ-Rural Development Programme in Baucau (Nov 2010 - Feb 2011). Semi-structured interviews were performed with seven female farmers and eleven experts (political and traditional local leaders and agricultural workers).

Results: Agricultural extension resulted in the formation of new working groups and a cooperative. Nevertheless the work is still organized in the same system of mutual help among relatives as before. Women stated that their labour time in rice cultivation has decreased with the new technique, while men's labour time has possibly risen. Despite this the interviewed women received more rice due to the increase in yield achieved through ICM. Gender-division of labour in rice production has become less rigid. All activities were done by women and men together except land preparation and use of machinery, which is exclusively done by men. It is recognized by the stakeholders that women are important for agricultural production, but their participation in agricultural training is restrained due to their obligation in domestic work. The rise in yield achieved through ICM has improved the household food security. Yet, it is unclear if women and men are equal partners in the decision on how the increased household income is used and if they benefit equally.

Conclusion: The implementation of ICM achieved an increase of rice yields, while at the same time reducing women's labour time. Yet, it remains unclear whether ICM has improved gender equality. Classic theses on the negative effect of agricultural innovation on women's status were confirmed: 1) Women's role as farmers is not fully recognized by extension workers (e.g. Boserup, 1982, Momsen, 1991), 2) Women's participation in rice cultivation declines with its intensification (e.g. Ember, 1983); 3) Newly introduced machinery is exclusively used by men (e.g. Ranga and Etz-Kowitz, 2010). The case hints that the practical implementation of GIZ gender guidelines urgently needs to be enforced.

Introduction

"In the morning women have to prepare breakfast for their husband [...].They help in the field for harvesting and transplanting rice. Then they have to prepare lunch, wash clothes, and prepare dinner. It is very difficult to manage all these activities. [...]Women have very big work compared to men, but this is our culture. People are already adapted to this culture and therefore it cannot be easily changed."

(Francisca de Fatima Soares, mayor of the village Soba, interview Dec 6th 2010)

In Timor-Leste most people live in subsistence based agriculture. 72 percent of the population of 1.1 million people live in rural areas. 80 percent of the labour force work in agriculture and 44 percent of the agricultural labour force are female (FAO, 2010). Yet, the current system of agricultural production fails to provide sufficient food supply. In 2006 64 percent of the population suffered from food insecurity (UNDP, 2006). Insufficient yields are caused by the effects of more than 20 years political instability as well as by poor land quality, low levels of technology and lacking access to resources, such as fertilizers or seeds. Estimates for the yield per hectare in rice production range from 1.5 to 3.1 t/ha (NSD and Ministry Of Finance, 2008, FAOSTAT, 2011) (compare Indonesia (5.0 t/ha) and South-Eastern-Asia (4.0 t/ha) (FAOSTAT, 2011)). The government compensates the resulting shortfall in domestic production of rice through costly imports and subsidized sales.

Together with the Ministry of Agriculture and Fisheries, GTZ (Gesellschaft für Technische Zusammenarbeit, now GIZ (Gesellschaft für Internationale Zusammenarbeit)) introduced a new system of rice cultivation in Timor-Leste. "Integrated Crop Management" (ICM) was first used in 2006/2007 and is now an integral part of the extension done by the Rural Development Program with the objective to shift from traditional subsistence farming to market oriented production (Kohl, 2009). Previous studies have shown that introduction of new technologies in agriculture can change gender-specific division of labour and gender relations within the households, often negatively affecting women (see paragraph 3 below). These results have led to efforts by national governments and international agencies to improve the outreach of agricultural extension to women and acknowledge women as key actors and stakeholders in agriculture. (WORLD BANK et al., 2009). Have these efforts been successful? Can the introduction of a new cultivation system, which has so often increased gender disparities, actually encourage gender equality? To answer this question the effects of agricultural extension on gender relations are analysed for the case of ICM in Timor-Leste.

Integrated Crop Management (ICM)

In this study Integrated Crop Management refers to a package of recommendations on rice cultivation as developed by researchers around V. Balasubramanian from the International Rice Research Institute, Philippines. The practical recommendations of ICM, as implemented in Timor-Leste, are a modification of those used in the system of rice intensification (SRI), which was developed in Madagascar in the late 1980s. Balasubramanian conducted on-farm evaluation of SRI in India, Indonesia, and the Philippines in the years 2000-02 and came to the conclusion that some SRI practices caused difficulties for the farmers and therefore introduced the following modifications:

-**Modified mat nursery:** Opposed to SRI, in which special trays are used for nurseries, the mat nursery recommended in ICM is established in the paddy field. A plastic sheet or a cover of banana leaves and rice husks builds the under layer to prevent the roots of the seedlings from growing too deep in the soil. The seedlings grow 14 to 15 days in the nursery, i.e. 2 to 4 days longer than in SRI.

-**Spacing:** 1 to 2 seedlings per hill are planted every 20 or 25 cm instead of only 1 seedling in 50 x 50 cm spacing.

-**Frequency of weeding:** ICM recommends the use of mechanical weeders 2-3 times during the growing period (1 time less often than in SRI). The purpose is besides the destruction of weeds more important soil aeration.

-**Soil nutrition:** Whereas SRI focuses on organic fertilizers, ICM recommends using mineral fertilizer when available. This is due to the fact than in Timor-Leste animal manure is not easily available (Heile et al., n.d., Balasubramanian et al., 2005, p. 65-66).

The overall decrease in labour time of women in ICM compared to techniques used before is due to the fact that the seedlings can be easier pulled out of the nursery before planting (Guterres, personal communication, 2011).

Theoretical Approach and Research Questions

A) Social aspects of rice cultivation: According to the analysis approach for development projects of Human Ecology, as presented by Teherani-Krönner (1989), agricultural production needs to be seen as one form of social interaction, the techniques of which are not only derived from ecological factors and availability of resources. Agricultural techniques are also influenced by the social environment. Living and working together requires organisation and cooperation. For this purpose a society creates institutions e.g. families, clans, religious communities or groups for mutual help in agricultural production. Accordingly individuals in a society do not only have material needs (e.g. the need to achieve sufficient yield for their own consumption), but also the need for social recognition (leading e.g. to the necessity to use parts of the yield for traditional ceremonies), (Teherani-Krönner, 1989, p.199-200). The aspect of multi-functionality of agricultural production with its economic, social and environmental function is highlighted in a comparable way in the IAASTD world agriculture report (IAASTD, 2009*).* The interdependence of agricultural production and social culture leads to the fact that none of the individual aspects can be analysed separately. Consequently in the present study it is asked: How do social environment and cultural beliefs influence rice cultivation?

The system of mutual help in rice production is analysed as an example of this interdependence. Collins claims that "wage labour and cash cropping lead to the breakdown of the very relationships that organize the subsistence production made necessary by the insufficient income they provide" (1986, p. 653). It is an objective of the Rural Development Programme to achieve market orientation of rice production through the implementation of ICM (Kohl, 2009) and ICM is supposed to decrease the amount of work needed for rice production (Guterres, personal communication 2011). Therefore it is asked: Has the introduction of ICM changed the system of mutual help in rice production? Have some workers lost a source of income?

B) Women as "invisible farmers": E. Boserup argues that division of labour is not "natural" and that the assumption of men working in the fields and women being only responsible for childcare and food preparation is a bias affected by western culture (1982). Many studies found that the work women did in agriculture was not recognized and coined the phrase of women being *"invisible farmers"* (amongst others Presvelou, 1975, Sachs, 1983). As a result of this oversight many agricultural development programmes address only men and only men profit from new technology while women's labour productivity declines relatively leading also to a lower social status (Boserup, 1982). Ranga and Etzkowitz argue that innovation itself is inherently gender biased, due to the social perception of technology linked to men rather than women (Ranga and Etzkowitz, 2010). To investigate if these theses still hold truth, it is questioned: Did the gender-specific division of tasks in rice cultivation change through the introduction of ICM? Are newly introduced technologies used by men or women? Are women recognized as key actors in agriculture and do they actively take part in ICM trainings?

C) Decline in women's participation in agriculture with its intensification: "The intensification of agriculture is associated with a relative decline in women's participation in agriculture" (Ember, 1983, p. 285). Ember argues that this is caused by an increase in "domestic work and fertility" (ibid). But the intensification of agriculture can also lead to a higher workload for women in activities in the field (e.g. the extension of the cultivation area leads to more work in weeding, which is usually done by women) or activities related to agriculture, most notably processing. These are activities, from which most of the times no personal income can be gained. Therefore development programmes that are designed to relieve women from their high labour burden by applying labour-saving technologies can have undesired results. "They can lead to changes in the division of labour within the household or to men taking over women's traditional industries when they become more profitable" (WORLD BANK et al 2009, p. 297). As saving labour time for women is one of the components of ICM, it is asked whether the introduction of ICM had negative effects on the participation of women in profitable activities:

How did women's working hours in rice cultivation change in comparison to men's? Has women's participation in agriculture relatively declined?

D) Distribution of income within households: "The traditional model of a ´household´, in which father, mother and children share common interests and work towards common goals," does not hold true in all societies (Jacobson, 1992, p. 11-12). As argued by Jacobson, women have the responsibility for feeding their families and are expected to secure the goods needed for household consumption, whereas men are more likely to spend their cash income for their personal consumption. Therefore it is wrong to assume that an increase in the income of a male household member will "mean an increase in total consumption by all family members (ibid, p. 13). Consequently it is asked: How is the increase in rice harvest used within the household? Who profits?

Method

Research was conducted during a three month placement in the Rural Development Program in Baucau. Interviews were conducted with the help of East-Timorese GIZ colleagues, who organised meetings and translated. Two villages in the district Baucau were selected for research: Soba in the sub-district Laga and Bado Ho'o in the sub-district Venilale. As there was no baseline study on gender arrangements available for this region, qualitative analysis was conducted in order to be able to look at a broader perspective of topics and find possible social effects of agricultural extension. In each village expert interviews were conducted in order to receive background information on the women's` socio-economic environment:

a) For Soba:

- Expert interviews with the mayor (one of the few female mayors in Timor-Leste), the traditional leader of Laga and the leader of a rice farming cooperative,
- Additional open interviews with one male farmer, one young woman and an owner of a rice milling machine

b) For Bado Ho'o:

- Expert interviews with the sub-district administrator of Venilale and with two women representatives of the village council,
- Group interviews with three women on their daily work routine

This information was used to design semi-structured interviews for seven female farmers. Information was supplemented by literature research and observation of agricultural trainings.

Characteristics of the interviewed female farmers

All but one of the interviewed women work in rice and dry land production and sell their produce (mainly vegetables, chicken, eggs and sometimes pigs) on the village market. The women from Bado Ho'o all live in households that own land for wet rice production, whereas none of the households of the women from Soba owns rice land. They work on their family`s or a cooperative's land and receive only a share of the yield for their work. The sales of agricultural produce are the only source of cash income for the households. The women are between 33 and 50 years old. They get married, when they were 21 to 26 years old. Six of the seven women come from a different village and moved to their husband's village, when they married. Yet, none of the women live in the same house as their parents in law. In five of the seven cases the husband's family paid a bride price (barlake) to the women's family. One did not want to answer this question and one woman from Bado Ho'o stated that her husband's family did not pay a bride price, because „the chief of village has already accepted modernization" (interview December 29th 2010). All women are mothers. They have three to eight children, two women have lost two respectively four children due to illness.

All seven women live in households, that participated in ICM training and implement ICM, but only four women participated in the training themselves. The amount of rice the households receive through their work ranges from 480 and more than 2,400 kg per year. The average size of the plots cultivated was 0.83 ha per household, i.e. -calculated for two adults per household- 0.42 ha/person. This means their size is close to the national average of 0.4 ha /person (UNDP, 2006). All households have in common that their share of yield increased drastically after the adoption of ICM: from an average of 2.2 t/ha to 4.1 t/ha. This equals an increase of nearly 90 percent and lies above the national average of 1.5 to 3.1 t/ha (NSD and MINISTRY OF FINANCE, 2008, FAOSTAT, 2011). Nevertheless three of the women's households still buy rice for at least one month per year, one does not buy nor sell and three households sell parts of their rice (two on the village market and one to a local cooperative). Hence four out of seven households in the interviewed group still produce in subsistence mode.

Discussion

A) Social aspects of rice cultivation: Nature is of great significance in East-Timorese ancestor belief. Special ceremonies (called Tarabandu) define regulations for the use of natural resources (expert interview, Dec 6th 2010), e.g. the banana leaves that are needed for building a mat nursery (expert interview, Jan 14th 2011). Also it was stated by HEILE that Timorese farmers would not take measures against rats in the rice field because of religious beliefs (personal communication, 2011). According to the cultural leader of one of the two research villages, there also used to be regulations on harvest time in rice cultivation but these are not used anymore. Also the gender-specific division of tasks in rice cultivation is not regulated by religious rules (interview, Dec 6th). Moreover, harvest ceremonies are conducted to give thanks to the ancestors and the amount of animals that need to be sacrificed for these ceremonies is regulated. Harvest ceremonies are an important social event in which the workers have a meal together. Here the religious occasion secures that the landowner or tenant has to give meat to his workers. Work in the rice field itself is seen as a social activity. Each working day the wife of the owner of the land or the tenant has to provide a meal that all workers take together. Nature is perceived in a religious way not in biological criteria. Interview partners were not concerned about possible effects of new technology, pesticides and fertilizer on the environment.

The forming of ICM groups and cooperatives did apparently not influence the composition of working groups that consist mostly of relatives of the landowner or tenant. It was stated by the cooperative leader and the cultural leader of Soba that these groups have not changed since the time of Portuguese colonization (i.e. before 1975). A cooperative leader from Soba stated that through the reduction of working time with ICM he now spends US$ 100 less for his workers. Also in Bado Ho'o interview partners mentioned that students were paid in cash for working on the fields. This indicates that some workers have lost cash income (expert interview, Jan 6th 2011; farmer interview, Jan 10th 2011). Yet, all interviewed female farmers received rice for their work or helped family members on a mutual basis. All said that their share of the yield had risen since the implementation of ICM. Moreover it was congruently stated that workers have the benefit of a family relation and the owners of the land respectively the tenants felt responsible for them. It can be concluded that land owners share the rising yield with their workers and work is paid in social rather than in economic scales. The important social function of the system of mutual help was illustrated in the case of a 20 year old orphan, who made her living by working on her uncle's fields and by doing this even had to support her younger brothers for their education (interview, Jan 14th 2011).

B) Women as invisible farmers: It was stated by the interview partners that the gender-specific division of tasks has become less rigid. Men now work in transplanting and harvest which were traditionally done by women. This could be due to a general trend of modernisation and rising gender-awareness in the country or due to the fact that working techniques changed through the introduction of ICM. Now more people are needed for transplanting to facilitate easy planting in line. ICM trainings also include the improvement of harvest techniques, e.g. to harvest when the rice stalks are dry. Also for this activity more workers are needed in order to finish the harvest quicker at the time of favourable weather conditions. When more people are needed at the same time, men may join because of practical reasons. Whereas men now participate in activities formerly done only by women, women do not work in tasks traditionally done by men. Land preparation and the preparing of bunds are still exclusively done by men. ICM does not necessarily include the use of machines. The technique ICM is used by women and men alike. Yet, the newly introduced mechanical weeders are operated by men. Not connected to ICM, hand tractors, threshing and milling machines are used in East-Timorese rice production. Hand tractors are operated exclusively by men. Data are missing on the gender of the operators and owners of threshing and milling machines. In the cases observed during research these were also owned and operated by men. It can be assumed that milling, an activity that was traditionally done by women, has been taken over by men once it became mechanised and a source of cash income. The fact that women were not included in training and handling of agricultural equipment shows that they are not recognized as key actors in agriculture, although it was uniformly stated in the expert interviews that women are important for agricultural production and women and men work together in rice production. Programs intended to create income for women often focus on food processing, weaving of traditional cloth or making clay pans. There are no trainings for women in vegetable production or marketing of agricultural produce. Only four of the seven interviewed women participated in the ICM trainings. The project even contributes to women not being able to attend trainings. It gives money to the ICM group so that they can prepare lunch for the day of the training. The women who then cook lunch do not get the chance to participate in the theoretical part of the training at the same time.

C) Decline in women's participation in agriculture with its intensification

All of the seven interviewed farmers said that they worked less in rice production since the implementation of ICM. The effect of ICM on men's working time is not clear. Since there is more attention paid to the levelling of the fields before planting, this activity could have become more labour-intensive for men. Also the weeding that is now done additionally is more often done by men. How ICM changed the amount of work needed for harvesting and transplanting was perceived differently by the interviewed women farmers. This is caused by the different techniques the women practised before they participated in ICM trainings. Some had to learn techniques like planting in line for the first time; some were already practicing similar techniques before. Solely the time needed for pulling out the seedlings before planting decreased according to all interviewed female farmers. It can be concluded that women's labour time in rice production decreased, while men's labour time has probably risen. Yet, it needs to be added that the use of hand tractors, milling and threshing machines has a bigger impact on working time reduction than ICM. Furthermore women also work in other agricultural activities next to rice production: they work in the vegetable garden, tend goats, pigs and chicken and sell their produce at the market. Only two women said that they used the time saved in rice production for domestic work, one said she worked more in the garden, the other four could not specify. Therefore it is not clear whether women's overall participation in agriculture has decreased or the decline in working in rice production was compensated by an increase in other agricultural work. Nevertheless it can be concluded that women are gradually pushed out of rice production, a sector that supported by policies is planned to become more market orientated and profitable.

D) **Distribution of income within households:** The households of the interviewed women use their rice harvest for their own consumption. Three of the seven households sell a surplus of their harvest. Two of them use the money for the costs of schooling of their children, one for school and for tradition. Asked whether they wished their sons or their daughters to get high education the six women farmers that were asked this question uniformly stated that there should be no discrimination between boys and girls. Confirming this, in the household expenditure on schooling, there could be found hardly any difference in the amount of money spend for girls` and boys` schooling. When asked what they would do if they could only afford education for one child, two of four stated that they would prefer a boy and two said that even then there should be no discrimination. This indicates relatively good gender awareness among the women. Results of literary research indicate a low status of women in rural households. Prevalence of domestic violence against women, patrilinear inheritance and also the conservative view of the Catholic Church could be seen as factors that bring forward subordination of women (Tids, 2007; Loch, 2007; Diamond, 2004). Yet, in the interviews little evidence could be found for this. The seven interviewed women said that they decided together with their husband on what to spend money. Moreover five of the seven women kept the money they earned at the market and their husbands asked them for cash whenever they needed. In one household the money was kept by the husband. In the remaining household each spouse kept his individual income (the wife selling fish and the husband selling rice). A possible result of further intensification of rice production could be that men take over large scale sale of rice and then manage the income instead of the women who now sell rice at the village market. It can be concluded that the rise of yield had a positive effect on the food security of the households as the women reported that they needed to buy additional rice during fewer months. It is difficult to judge if husband and wife are equal partners in the decision making on household expenditures. At least in some interviews with female farmers this seemed to be the case, but the individual relationships of course differ. It has to be feared that women will lose their income from selling rice at the village market with a further development to selling larger quantities.

Conclusion

The Rural Development Project has been successful with the implementation of ICM in increasing yields and therefore contributing to food security. The interviewed women also felt that they have benefitted from ICM through the increase in yield and the reduction of their working hours. Yet, the process of intensification in agriculture can also have negative effects. The results of the interviews conducted indicate that Timor-Leste is at the beginning of this process: in the interviewed households agriculture is still practiced mainly for subsistence and the products are sold at the local village market. This ensures that women, whose task it is to sell the products, have access to cash and a bigger influence in decision making within the household. Furthermore the system of mutual help is still practiced as before. Further market orientation puts this social system at risk. Therefore it is alarming that extension work does not integrate gender aspects. Gender theories are by now widely recognized among institutions, by GIZ as well as the Ministry of Agriculture of Timor-Leste. Yet, in practice, the implementation of ICM principles does not work. The interviewed women are still 'invisible farmers' and are discriminated in their participation in agricultural trainings. Theories on the negative effect of intensification in agriculture on women's status were uniformly confirmed.

A reason for this might be that the highly theoretical approach of gender studies is not sufficiently translated into practical recommendations as its importance is difficult to understand for agricultural extension workers. Measures to better include women in the process of market orientation in agriculture would be for instance a better timing of trainings or extra trainings only for women, wherever it is asked for. Furthermore it is important to support women in sectors, where they can build on practical knowledge, in the case of Timor-Leste e.g. vegetable production and marketing.

Acknowledgements

I want to thank the GIZ-RDP Timor-Leste team Baucau for the warm welcome I received and for the help for my research work, especially: Mr. Heile, Mr. Benjamin, Miss Amalda, Miss Rosa, Mrs. Linda, Miss Neny and the centre team, Mr. Felix and Mr. Chiquito.

Informants:

GUTERRES, Benjamin   Farming systems coordinator GIZ-RDP Eastern Districts, Timor-Leste

HEILE, Heinz-Josef   Officer responsible for contracts and cooperation GIZ- 'Employment Promotion for Young People' Timor-Leste, coordinator for GIZ-Rural Development Programme Eastern districts , Timor-Leste

Literature:

BALASUBRAMANIAN, V.: ICM-Timor-Leste: Issues and Updates: A Note to the Honorable Minister, MAP. Dili, Timor Leste, 2010.

BOSERUP, E.: Die ökonomische Rolle der Frau in Afrika, Asien, Lateinamerika. Stuttgart, 1982.

COLLINS, J. L.: The Household and Relations of Production in Southern Peru. Comparative Studies in Society and History, **28,4,1**, 651–671, 1986.

DIAMOND, N. K.: Gender Assessment for USAID/Timor-Leste Country Strategy Plan FY 2004-2009. (accessed April 12th 2011, available at: http://www.usaid.gov/our_work/cross-cutting_programs/wid/pubs/ga_easttimor.pdf), 2004.

EMBER, C. R.: The Relative Decline in Women's Contribution to Agriculture with Intensification. American Anthropologist, **85**, 285–304, 1983.

FAO: Country Profile: Food Security Indicators: Country: Timor-Leste. (accessed June 18th 2011, available at: http://www.fao.org/fileadmin/templates/ess/documents/food_security_statistics/country_profiles/eng/Timor-Leste_E.pdf), 2010.

FAOSTAT: Production Crops. (accessed April 12th 2011, available at: http://faostat.fao.org/site/567/DesktopDefault.aspx?PageID=567#ancor) , 2011.

HEILE, H., GUTERRES, B., DEICHERT, G. and BARROS, J.: Good Agricultural Practices Crop Production: Irrigated Rice, ICM and SRI. GTZ Timor-Leste. not published

IAASTD: Agriculture at a Crossroads Synthesis Report. IAASTD (accessed June 7th 2011, available at: http://www.agassessment.org/reports/IAASTD/EN/Agriculture%20at%20a%20Crossroads_Syn thesis%20Report%20(English).pdf) , 2009.

JACOBSON, J. L.: Gender Bias: Roadblock to Sustainable Development. Worldwatch Institute, Washington, D.C., 1992.

KOHL, G.: Fortschrittsbericht zu einer TZ-Maßnahme: Förderung der Ländlichen Entwicklung Timor-Leste, PN: 2005.2137.7.GTZ, Timor-Leste, 2009.

LOCH, A.: Haus, Handy & Halleluja: Psychosoziale Rekonstruktion in Osttimor : eine ethnopsychologische Studie zur postkonfliktuösen Dynamik im Spannungsfeld von Identität, Trauma, Kultur und Entwicklung. IKO, Verlag für Interkulturelle Kommunikation, Frankfurt am Main, 2007.

MOMSEN, J. H.: Women and work in rural areas. - In: MOMSEN, J. H. (Ed) Women and development in the Third World. Routledge, London, 1991.

NATIONAL STATISTICS DIRECTORATE (NSD) [TIMOR-LESTE] and MINISTRY OF FINANCE [TIMOR-LESTE]: Timor-Leste Survey of Living Standards 2007: Final Statistical Abstract. (accessed Feb 24th 2011, available at: http://dne.mof.gov.tl/TLSLS/Publication/finalstatisticalabstract.pdf), 2008.

PRESVELOU, C.: The invisible woman. CERES, 2, 50–53, 1975.

RANGA, M. and ETZKOWITZ, H.: Athena in the world of Techne: The Gender Dimension of Technology, Innovation and Entrepreneurship. Journal of Technology, Management and Innovation 5, 1– 12, 2010.

SACHS, C. E.: The invisible farmers: Women in agricultural production. Rowman & Allanheld, Totowa, N.J., 1983.

TEHERANI-KRÖNNER, P.: Humanökologisch orientierte Entwicklungsprojekte. - In: GLAESER, B. (Ed): Humanökologie. Westdt. Verl., 195–208, 1989.

TIMOR INSTITUTE OF DEVELOPMENT STUDIES (TIDS): Baseline Study on Feminization of Poverty in Timor-Leste: Deprivation of Women across Sectors. Programme for Enhancing Rural Women's Leadership and Participation in Nation Building in Timor-Leste. UNIFEM, Dili, 2007.

UNDP: Timor- Leste Human Developmet Report 2006: The Path out of Poverty- Integrated rural development. (accessed April 4th 2011, available at: http://hdr.undp.org/en/reports/national/asiathepacific/timorleste/TIMOR_LESTE_2006_en.pd f), 2006.

WORLD BANK, FAO and IFAD: Gender in Agriculture Sourcebook. (accessed Feb 24th 2011, available at: http://siteresources.worldbank.org/INTGENAGRLIVSOUBOOK/Resources/CompleteBook.pdf) 2009.

Export Potential of Rice from Pakistan

Altaf Hussain

International Society for Sustainable Development and Agriculture, Göttingen, Germany
E-Mail:ahussai@t-online.de, Tel.:+49 (0) 55133297; Fax:+49 (0) 5513098673

Abstract

Agriculture is said to be the backbone of Pakistan's economy. It provides the means of livelihood for about 68 % of the population and engages 44.7 % of the total workforce. It also contributes 21.8 % of the total output (GDP) and supplies raw materials to industry. Rice is the second important food crop after wheat in Pakistan and accounts for the most part of the consumption of Pakistan's population. As foreign exchange earnings are essential for the development of the country, Pakistan has to export surplus rice. It ranks fifth among the rice exporting countries in the world, after Thailand (27.7 %), India (16 %), Vietnam (14.3 %) and USA (13.3 %). The average growth rates of the area cultivated with rice stood by 0.5 %, rice production by 2 % and yield per hectare by 2 %. The main export item is Basmati rice. The cultivated area under the Basmati rice rose at an average rate of 1.58 % in the last years. The output increased by about 5 % and the yield per hectare by 3.14 % during last years. The yield per hectare is lower as compared to other rice growing countries, such as Egypt, India, Bangladesh, Burma, Japan, Vietnam and USA. The main causes of low yields are late maturity, less plant population, low fertilizer response and inadequate irrigation facilities. The major export markets of Pakistani rice are USA, Germany, Japan, UK, Hong Kong, Saudi Arab and Dubai. This paper attempts to provide and build up some of the necessary information on the supply and demand for Pakistan's fine rice. Moreover, the rationality of increasing the production and exports of fine rice and of continuing the present policy and institutional framework for the procurement and export of the rice, in examined. The paper is divided into four parts, in addition to the introduction and conclusion: 1) Supply potential of fine rice; 2) Potential world demand for fine rice; 3) Policy and institutional framework for the procurement and export of fine rice and 4) Rationality of increasing the production and export of fine rice. There are many varieties of rice grown in the former Punjab and Sind areas. Pakistani Basmati rice has a good cooking quality. In Punjab province, the rice growing areas are: Gujranwala, Sheikhupura, Lahore and Sialkot.

1. Introduction

Rice is the most important staple food for a large part of the world population. According to FAO Statistics of 2011, rice is the grain with the second highest worldwide production, after maize. Its annual yield worldwide is approximately 535 million tons. Fifty countries produce rice, with China and India support 50 percent of total production. Southeast Asian countries separately support an annual production rate of 23 million metric tons of which they export very little. Pakistan being an agro-based economy has natural abundance of all agricultural products including food items. Rice is the third largest crop after wheat and cotton. It is grown over 10 percent of the total cropped area. Rice is a highly valued cash crop and is also a major export item. It accounts for 6.7 percent in value added in agriculture and

1.6 percent of GDP. Pakistan grows enough high quality rice to meet both domestic demand and allow for exports of around one million tons per annum. Average rice yield in Pakistan, is comparatively low compared to China, USA, North Korea, South Korea, India, Bangladesh, Vietnam, Philippines, Brazil, Egypt, Iran, etc. It needs to increase yields in order to sustain food security at home and maintain its share in world markets. The quality of produce suffers due to defective harvesting methods, out-dated processing technology and admixtures during various stages of processing and marketing.

Trading in rice both in domestic and international markets has become more quality conscious. Even in the local markets buyers now demand quality rice. In order to meet the challenges under the WTO regime, it is now essential for the country to put together its rice production and marketing strategies to match the demand of international markets.

2. Potential World Demand for Rice

2.1 International Scenario

Information on world production, consumption, stocks and trade of rice is compiled in the following tables.

Table 2.1.1: World production, consumption, stocks and trade of rice, 2007 to 2011 (000 metric tons)

	2007	2008	2009	2010	2011
Production	432,210	447,498	440,525	451,216	461,394
Consumption	427,402	435,931	437,858	447,478	475, 25
Ending Stock	79,031	90,556	93,016	96,424	100,247
Trade	29,763	29,335	31,607	34,363	32,920

Source: World Market & Trade, USDA, 2011

Table 2.1.2: World production, consumption, stocks and trade of rice, 2009 & 2011 (percentage change)

	2009	2011	Change	% change
Production	440,525	461,394	20,869	4.37
Consumption	437,858	475,325	37,467	8.55
Ending Stock	93,016	100,247	7,231	22.87
Trade	31,607	32,920	1,153	3.64

Source: World Market & Trade, USDA, 2011

The world rice production in 2011 increased to 461 million t from 440 million t in 2009 showing an increase of 4.37 percent. The consumption increased from 475 million t in 2011 to 438 million t in 2009 – thus registering an increase of 8.55 percent. The ending stocks in 2011 were 100 million t showing an increase of 22.87 percent over 2009 while trade increased by 1,1 million t , i.e. from 31,6 million to 32,9 million t which shows an increase in percentage over 3.64 percent respectively.

2.2 World Top Exporters of Rice

The world ten top rice exporting countries in the year 2010-2011 in term of export value were :-
Thailand, Vietnam, Pakistan, United States, India, China, Uruguay, Cambodia, Egypt and Burma.

Table 2.2.1: Trend in World Rice Export, 2000 to 2012 (1000 metric tons)

Country	2000	2006/2007	2007/2008	2008/2009	2009/2010	2010/12011	2011/2012
Thailand	6,543	8,250	10,011	8,570	9,047	10,500	8,000
Vietnam	3,370	4,700	4,649	5,950	6,734	7,000	6,700
USA	2,756	3,267	3,170	3,868	3,250	3,050	3,050
Pakistan	2026	3,000	3,050	3,187	4,000	2,800	3,750
China	2,951	1,000	969	783	619	500	600
India	1,449	4,300	3,363	2,123	2,052	3,800	4,500
Uruguay	642	625	742	926	808	975	850
Australia	617	100	408	17	350	600	650
Burma	159	150	511	1,052	445	900	750
EU	308	150	157	150	282	300	350
Argentina	473	400	408	594	468	600	600
Guyana	167	170	185	244	275	23	230
Egypt		900	750	575	570	80	500
Japan		200	200	200	200	200	150
Cambodia		450	500	800	1,000	1,000	800
Others	785	365	392	556	755	864	690
World Total	22,872		29,763	29,335	31,363	34,363	32,920

Source: USDA, Foreign Agricultural Service (FAS), November 2011

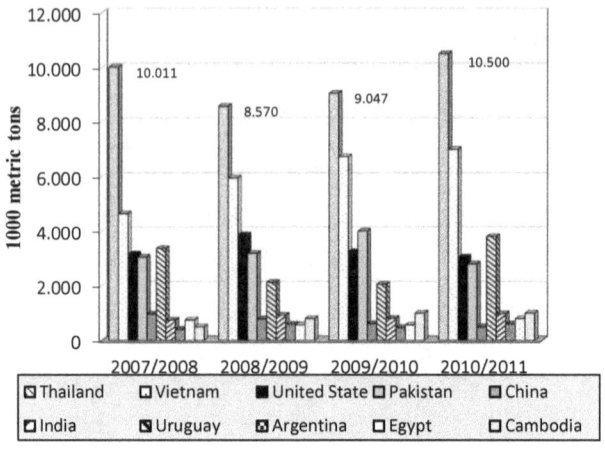

Figure 1 Trend in World Rice Export 2007/08 to 2010/11(000metric tons)
Source: USDA, Foreign Agricultural Service (FAS), November 2011

2.3 World Top Imports of Rice

The world ten top rice importing countries in the year 2011 in term of value were: Philippines, UAE, Saudi Arabia, Iran, Malaysia, Senegal, UK, USA, France and Bangladesh.

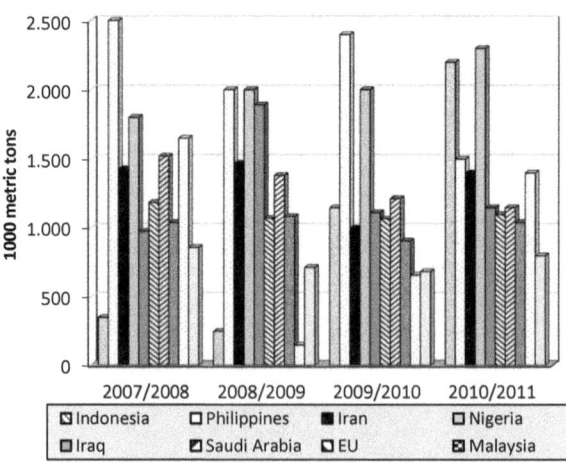

Figure 2: Trends in World Rice Import, 2007/08 to 2010/11 (1000 metric tons)
Source: USDA, Foreign Agricultural Service (FAS), November 2011

Table 2.3.1: Trends in World Rice Import 2000 to 2011/12 (000 metric tons)

Country	2000	2006/2007	2007/2008	2008/2009	2009/2010	2010/2011	2011/2012
Indonesia	1,500	600	350	250	1,150	2,200	1,400
Iran	1,100	900	1,430	1,470	1,000	1,400	1,500
Nigeria	1,200	1.700	1,800	2,000	2,000	2,300	2,150
Iraq	1,274	1,000	975	1,89	1,140	1,150	1,2001
Saudi Arabia	992	650	1,186	1,072	1,069	1,100	1,150
Philippines	900	1,850	2,500	2,000	2,400	1,500	2,200
EU	852	925	1,520	1,383	1,216	1,150	1,070
Japan	656	650	533	750	649	700	700
Senegal	700	850	860	715	685	800	750
Malaysia	596	850	1,039	1,086	907	1,040	1,130
Cote d"Ivoire	550	0800	800	800	840	900	950
South Africa	525	800	650	745	733	760	750
Bengladesh		600	1,650	150	660	1,400	750
Senegal		850	860	715	685	800	700
Brazil	612	800	471	650	778	500	500
Others	4,215	6,956	8,199	7,882	8,799	8,887	8,872
World Total	22,872	27,960	29,763	29,335	31,607	34,368	32,920

Source: USDA, Foreign Agricultural Service (FAS), November 2011

2.4 World Rice Production and Consumption 2002 – 2012

The total world rice production in the year of 2011/2012 amounted to 461,394 thousand metric tons. China´s produced 139,000 thousand tons and India 100,000 thousand tons.

Table 2.4: World Rice Production 2007/08 to 2011/12 (1000 metric tons)

Country	2007/2008	2008/2009	2009/2010	2010/2011	2011/2012
China	130,224	134,330	136,570	137,000	139,000
India	96,950	99,180	89,90	95,300	100,000
Indonesia	37,000	38,310	36,370	37,060	37,300
Bangladesh	28,800	31,000	31,000	32,900	33,000
Vietnam	24,375	24,393	24,993	26,075	25,430
Burma	10,730	10,150	10,550	10,750	11,000
Japan	7,930	8,023	7,711	7,720	7,680
Thailand	19,800	19,850	20,250	20,262	21,250
Philippines	10,479	10,775	9,772	10,539	10,650
Brazil	8,199	8,570	7,929	9,257	8,840
Pakistan	5,700	4,843	4,916	4,295	4,240
South Korea	4,408	4,843	4,916	4,295	4,240
Others	30,824	33,493	35,701	37,083	37,556
World Total	432,210	447,498	440,525	451,216	461,394

Source: USDA, Foreign Agricultural Service (FAS), November 2011

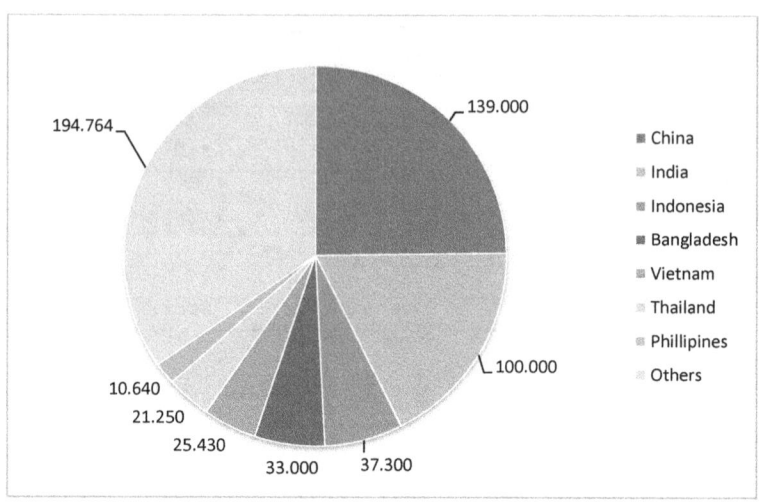

Figure 3: World Rice Production of major Countries in 2011
Source: USDA, Foreign Agricultural Service (FAS), November 2011

The total rice consumption of the world amounted to 475,326 thousand metric tons in the year of 2011/2012. China's consumption amounted to 137,000 thousand tons and India was second with a total consumption of 94,000 thousand tons.

Table 2.4.2: World Rice Consumption 20001/02 to 2011/2012 (000 metric tons)

Country	2001/2002	2007/2008	20082009	2009/2010	2010/2011	2011/2012
China	136,110	127,420	133,000	134,320	135,000	137,000
India	85,000	90,465	91,090	85,650	90,000	94,000
Indonesia	36,58	36,350	37,100	38,000	39,000	39,550
Bangladesh	24,25	30,747	31,000	31,600	33,800	34,200
Vietnam	17,100	19,400	19,000	19,150	19,300	19,550
Burma	9,450	10,249	9,648	9,850	9,850	10,250
Japan	9,300	8,162	8,326	8,200	8,125	8,250
Thailand	10,000	9,600	10,200	10,500	10,500	10700
Philippines	8,815	13,449	13,100	13,125	13,150	13,175
Brazil	8,000	8,350	8,400	8,477	8,400	8,500
Iran	3,000	3,100	2,950	2,900	3,000	3,000
South Korea		4,670	4,768	4,765	4,797	4,800
World Total	405,856	427,402	435,931	437,858	447,478	475,326

Source: USDA, Foreign Agricultural Service (FAS), November 2011

50

3. Supply Potential of Rice

3.1 Varieties of Rice Grown in Pakistan

Different varieties of rice are grown in Pakistan, for example, Super Basmati, Basmati PK-385, Irri-6, Irri-9 and KS-282. Pakistan is primarily known for its aromatic rice (Super Basmati/Basmati PK-385).Two varieties of rice dominate the market: Basmati, which is mainly grown in Punjab and Irri, which is mainly grown in Punjab and Sindh. Basmati accounts for 2 percent of exports and is of a higher quality than Irri. Since 1987/88, the government allowed rice export also by the private sector. Before this, the Rice Export Corporation of Pakistan (RECP) was exclusively handling rice export of Pakistan.

3.2 Provincial Shares in Area and Production

The annual production of rice from 2006/07 to 2008/9 has an average of 5.984 million tones and area of 2,679 thousand ha. The provincial shares in area and production of rice by variety are as under:

Table 3.2.1: Pakistan Area and Production of Rice, Average of 2006/07 to 2008/09

Variety	Area (1000 ha)	%	Production (1000 t)	%
Basmati	1458,57	54.45	2502,93	41.83
IRRI	880,55	32.87	2692,67	44.99
Others	339,80	12.68	788,79	13.18
Total	2678,93	100	5983,93	100

The average total rice production in Pakistan was 5,984 thousand tons from 2006/07 to 2008/09 on a total area of 2,679 thousand hectares. Basmati rice production was 2,502 thousand tons on an area of 1,459 thousand hectares, IRRI was 2,693 thousand tons on an area of 880 thousand hectares, the figures for other varieties of rice were 789 thousand tons on an area of 340 thousand hectares. The provincial shares of production of rice in percentage i.e. Punjab 56 percent, Sindh 34 percent, Kpakha 2 percent, and Balochistan 8 percent.

3.3 Short-term Changes: 2007/08 and 2008/09

The provincial changes in area, yield and production of rice for 2008/09 crop over 2007/08 crop are as under.

Table 3.3.1 Area, Yield and Production of Rice by Variety: 2007/08 and 2008/09, Total Pakistan

	2007/2008	2008/2009	% change
Area (1000 ha)	2515,4	2940	16.9
Yield (kg/ha)	2212	2364	6.9
Production (1000 t)	5563,4	6850	24.9

Source: Rice Export Association of Pakistan (REAP)

The above table shows that during 2008/09, the total production of rice at the country level increased by 24.9 percent solely due to 16.9 percent expansion in area and 6.9 percent improvement in yield. The production of basmati rice has increased by 4.4 percent entirely because of expansion in area whereas the yield fell by 5.7 percent. The production of IRRI has increased by 27.3 percent as a result of 14.6 percent increase in area and 11.1 percent improvement in yield. Similarly production of other varieties of rice has gone up by 93.5 percent as result of 50.5 percent increase in area and 28.6 percent improvement in yield. According to United States Department of Agriculture (USDA) Foreign Agricultural Service the World rice yield in 2009 was 4.25 m/ha, while in China it was 6.56, India 3.38, Bangladesh 4.01, Vietnam 5.05, Philippines 3.77, Egypt 10.04 and in Iran 3.95.

3.4 Target vs. Achievement: 2008/09 Crop

During 2008/09 crop year, rice production exceeded the target by 21.5 percent mainly due to the increase in area by 13.3 percent and yield by 7.2 percent over the respective targets. The Basmati production has fallen short of the target by 4.0 percent because of decline in yield by 6.2 percent though the area has gone beyond the target by 2.4percent. The production of IRRI and other varieties has exceeded its target by 43.7 percent, because area and yield have gone up by 28.1 and 12.2 percent respectively. During 2008/09 in the province of Punjab the production exceeded the target by 9.5 percent. The yield target fell down by 2.3 percent and area target exceeded the target by 12.1 percent. In the Province of Sindh the production exceeded the target by 44.7 percent, the yield by 14.2 percent and area by 26.9 percent. In the province of NWFP the target was achieved during the year 2008/09. While in the Balochistan Province the production exceeded the target by 22 .6percent, the yield by 35.4percent while the area decreased by 9.5percent.

Table 3.4: Pakistan's Targets and Achievements: 2008/09

	Target	Achievement	% change
Area (1000 ha)	2494	2940,2	13.3
Yield (kg/ha)	2205	2364	7.2
Production (1000 t)	5720	6950	21.5

Source: Rice Export Association of Pakistan (REAP)

4. Analysis of Pakistan's Rice Export Markets

4.1 Pakistan Rice Export for Last Five Years

The rice export details for the last five years are given in the table below:-

Table 4.1: Pakistan Rice Export for last five years (1000 metric tons)

2006/2007	2007/2008	2008/2009	2009/2010	2010/2011
3,000	3,187	4,000	2,800	3,750

Source: Rice Export Association of Pakistan (REAP)

The quantity of rice exported increased to 3,1 t in the year 2007/2008 from 3 million t in 2006/2007. In the year 2010/2011 the quantity of rice increased to 3,7 million t from 3.0 million t in the year 2006/2007 respectively.

There is a huge decrease in the year 2009/2010 to 2,8 million t from 4 million t in the year 2008/2009. The reason for the decrease in 2008 was the decrease in demand in international markets, decrease in international price of rice, government intervention in the local market and a decelerating trend in private sector credit disbursement. In the year 2008, the importing countries purchased huge quantities of rice on the perception that international prices would go up. Due to availability of stocks in the importing countries, the demand for rice has decreased considerably. Due to this decrease in demand of rice, the price in the international market has gone down. Pakistan's exports of rice are also passing though this phase. Pakistan's exports of rice are controlled by the private sector; however, recently TCP has floated an international tender for the sale of rice. Owing to this, the prices of rice will decrease and private entrepreneurs will not be able to compete in international markets with other exporting countries like Thailand and Vietnam. Due to bumper production of rice in 2008, the stocks have piled up due to lower international prices and lesser demand. The exporters have also faced problems in repayment of loans due to this reason. After the new crop in 2009, there is also a cash flow problem for traders. Pakistan's increasing and decreasing share in the world rice market can be seen in the figure given below:

Table 4.1.2 Pakistan's Increasing/Decreasing Share in World Market
2006 – 2011 (2006/2007 = 100%)

Year	Amount (1000 t)	Change (1000 t)	Change (%)
2006/2007	3,000		
2007/2008	3,187	+187	+6.2
2008/2009	4,000	+813	+27,1
2009/2010	2,800	-1,200	-40,0
2010/2011	3,750	+950	31,7

Source: Rice Export Association of Pakistan (REAP)

4.2 Supply Chain Issues

1. Lack of supplies of certified seeds.
2. To acquire the desired number of plants per acre, skilled labour is not engaged for transplanting of nursery under strict vigilance.
3. Lining of irrigation canals, distributaries and on-farm water channels are not properly managed.
4. Power tariffs are on higher side which makes the tube-well irrigation expensive.
5. Proper machinery is not being used by the farmers in harvesting and threshing, which results in damage to the quality of rice.
6. Storage capacities for exports are insufficient.
7. Prices of fertilizers and pesticides are on higher side.
8. Old traditional system to dry the paddy rice on open space is still in practice.
9. Lack of marketing strategy.

4.3 Pakistan's Opportunities and Shortcomings in Rice Trade

To enhance the rice trade Pakistan has the opportunities that:

1. India has imposed a ban on exports of non-Basmati rice this year because of low production. To meet its local demand, India is planning to import non-Basmati rice from other countries. India is also negotiating with three countries for import of rice, which will increase the demand of rice in the international market.
2. Pakistan has an opportunity to sell his rice products in the Philippines. That is a huge potential for Pakistani rice.
3. Despite the demand of rice in South Africa, Senegal, Saudi Arabia, Kuwait, USA, Turkey, Sri Lanka, Australia, Malaysia, Indonesia and the Philippines, Pakistan has a small share in these markets.
4. Pakistan should remove the shortcomings to compete in the world rice market accordingly.
5. Pakistan's rice is famous in the world but mixing of one variety with another affects the quality of rice which results in loss of market.
6. The use of low technology both at harvesting/threshing and milling level results in huge quantity of broken rice.
7. Most Pakistani exporting companies are selling rice without any brand name. Due to this the exporters do not get a good price for even high quality product.
8. Pakistan is selling rice in bulk quantity. Pakistani exporters are not selling rice in packing of 1 kg, 2 kg and 5 kg which results in lower price.
9. All seed varieties being used by the private sector are not approved by the Government which results in poor quality and lesser yield.

4.4 Analysis of Potential of Rice Importing Countries for Export Rice from Pakistan

To enhance the rice export potential for Pakistani rice, it is necessary to adopt some immediate measures to win the new market in the world. The markets of the countries like South Africa, Senegal, UAE, USA, UK, Belgium, Germany, Turkey, Indonesia, Malaysia and Australia have to be overviewed and measures should be adopted to search for possibilities to export rice from Pakistan. In view of the potential of the above mentioned markets for exports, there is a need to enhance the export promotional activities in these markets. It is necessary to-1) Allow the import of rice harvesters without duty from any country of origin. 2) Discourage harvesting of immature paddy with punitive action. 3) Add information on proper harvesting methods and their importance to the awareness program. 4) Imported and locally manufactured paddy dryers must be given relief in taxes, levies and duties to meet the needs of millers all over Pakistan. 5) Millers should be encouraged to install parboiled rice units to meet the demand of parboiled rice in the world. 6) To promote rice exports, the storage capacity at the export points should be enhanced. 7) Proper system of disbursement of private sector credit for rice exporters may be developed. 8) The Ministry of Food and Agriculture Islamabad may be requested to seek technical advice from the International Rice Research Institute, Philippines for increasing production and yield of rice in Pakistan.

References

AMAD: Agricultural Market Access Database. (AMAD). Online:www.amad.net

Bhasin, V. K.: India and the Emerging Global Rice Trade, PICRIC. Limited, New Delhi, India, 2004.

Cape, C.: International trade in rice: Recent developments and prospects, International Rice Research Institute (IRRI), 2005.

E.J. Wailes, M. Ataman Aksoy and John C. Beghin: Rice: global trade, protectionist, policies and the impact of trade liberalization, 2005.

Foreign Agricultural Services/USDA: Foreign Agricultural Services /USDA Office of Global Analysis, 2011.

MA, A.: Global agricultural trade and developing countries, World Bank, New York, 2005.

Pakistan: Pakistan economic survey 2010/2011, Government of Pakistan, Islamabad, 2011.

Pakistan: Federal Bureau of Statistics, Annual Report, Islamabad, Pakistan, 2011.

REAP: Rice Export Association of Pakistan (REAP) Yearly Report, 2010.

Sind Board Of Investment: Prefeasibility, parboil rice processing venture in Sind, Pakistan, Sind Board of Investment, Government of Sind, Pakistan 2010.

TDAP: Trade Development Authority of Pakistan, Report on "Potential markets of Rice" Pakistan, 2010

Thai Rice Exporters Association: Annual report "Thai Rice Exporters Association "Bangkok, Thailand, 2011.

USDA PS&D (U.S. Department of Agriculture, Production, Supply and Distribution). 2010.

USDA, FAS: "Rice. Annual". Various years and countries. Global Agricultural Information Network (GAIN) Reports, Foreign Agricultural Service (FAS),Washington, D.C., 2010.

Food Security at the Crossroads Anno 1864, 1894, 1924, 1954, 1984, 2014, 2044, 2074. A Wake up Call!

Manfred Kern

agriExcellence GmbH, 55296 Lörzweiler, Germany, info@agriexcellence.de

Abstract

Food security has top priority today and in future. There is no discussion about the fact that everybody must eat. Nevertheless, this fundamental need was globally addressed by the United Nations in the Universal Declaration of Human Rights in 1948, Article 25: "Everyone has the right to a standard of living adequate for the health and well-being of himself and of his family, including food, clothing, housing and medical care and necessary services ...," (United Nations, 1948). At the beginning of the Third Millennium, we all know that this human right is not being realized worldwide.

The right to adequate nourishment is considered to have been violated if consistent deprivation of food or food sources has brought about a violation of human dignity. In view of the numbers of starving people– estimated by the FAO at 1,000,000,000 worldwide – and of the many thousands of people dying of hunger every day, this is doubtless one of the human rights which have been most flagrantly violated over many decades. Moreover, it has been shown time and again that it is not possible to implement rights to freedom unless the right to nourishment has been realized. And vice versa, violations of economic or cultural rights – e.g. forcible displacement, prohibition of free practice of religion or deprivation of food sources – generally go hand in hand with violations of civil or political rights.

A brief look back over the last 150 years and the outlook for the next 60 years, compressed into a time frame of 30 years each, will provide an outline of conditions, backgrounds and intentions with respect to Article 25 of the Universal Declaration of Human Rights. A wake up call and an action list will be presented in order to improve food security (availability, accessibility, affordability, acceptability) as quickly as possible in order to realize Article 25 of the Human Rights Declaration.

Food Security at the Crossroads

Anno 1864: A valuable source of information about the food security situation in 1864 is the book: The Source of Gold or: The Farmer on the Path of Progress - A Narrative for the Common Folk as a Contribution to Promoting an Agriculture in Keeping with our Times written by Heinrich Schwerdt in 1859.

1894: The main reason why people emigrated from the Eifel in Germany during the nineteenth century was: "... the unfavourable climatic conditions, the quality of the Eifel soils and the suitability or unsuitability of the crops grown there – from cereals to potatoes – showed that it was no easy task for the people in the Eifel to earn a livelihood. They lived in a region where the basic requirements for survival gave rise to constant uncertainty, brought about hunger and made it necessary to emigrate" (Pracht, H.-P., 1998).

1924: "The world has changed. Our age is totally unlike any which has gone before. There is no longer any such thing as isolation; all gaps have been removed. Nowadays an individual family will emigrate, moving back and forth across the world without any major hindrances in the search for better opportunities. Modern trade has brought about great changes in the world situation.

Where 1,750 million people are on the search for nourishment, will any of them have time to take things easy? Most certainly not! How bad will the situation become for the majority of the human race when the world's population rises to 3,500 million, a number which at the present rate will be reached before the year 2000? ... and the importance of agriculture was ignored." described by East, E. M. (1926). Relevant answers were given by Paul de Kruif (1928).

1954: "Hunger is the central problem of our time", wrote W. Greiling in 1954. "Hunger highlights the mistakes of our time and our world. Hunger on earth (600 million people) is a very special tragedy. It is not unavoidable. The means to overcome hunger are available, but they are not used. The rest of the world could help easily. But the rest of the world is doing more or less nothing."

1984: "Looking into the future, we can foresee that twenty years from now most of the crops we know today will be grown from plants that have been "improved" or reinvented in some way in a genetics laboratory. Many other crops will be improved by conventional plant-breeding techniques. But this will be done with a degree of precision and efficiency unimaginable just a few years ago. What used to take breeders many years to achieve - and nature many thousands of years - will be done in months or even weeks! These laboratory crops will be small miracles of applied research. They will be specially bred to grow faster; to ripen at a particular time; to resist disease, drought, or frost; to make better use of sunlight or fertilizers. They will, in short, be just what the farmer ordered." addressed in Walt Disney World (1984).

An additional interesting guide is given by John W. Rosenblum, (1983).

Furthermore, "History has taught us that wars produce hunger, but we are less aware that mass poverty can lead to war or end in chaos. Where hunger rules, peace cannot prevail." (Willy Brandt). Rising food prices lead to a level of instability which may in turn become critical for the maintenance of national or regional security.

"Hunger still stalks far too many poor people today. Expanding the reach of improved crop technologies to areas of the globe passed over by the "green revolution" combined with foreseeable improvements in crop productivity will make it possible to provide a better diet at lower prices to more people in the future. The prospect for feeding a world of 10 billion people, while challenging, is bright." "You cannot build peace on empty stomachs (Lord Orr, J.B., FAO)" was outlined by Norman Borlaug in 1970.

It's a historical truth that when food prices rise, conflict increases. So it's no wonder that the spike in the cost of agricultural commodities in recent years (2008) has been a contributing factor to revolution in the Middle East and North Africa (2011, 2012). In Pakistan, people began exhibiting "extraordinary behaviours" due to a high prevalence of food insecurity – selling kidneys, bonded labour, selling children, and committing suicide because they could not support their families as reported by E. Hooper in 2010.

2014: In 1974, the mighty of this world came together for their first World Food Conference. At that time 920 million people were starving – and the good tidings ran: "Within a decade no man, woman or child will go to bed hungry." Nothing of the sort! 22 years later, in 1996, the FAO still registered 840 million undernourished people – and soon it was time for the next hunger summit. As though the heads of state wanted to come to terms with the plague, they contented themselves then in Rome at least with the objective / 'promise' to halve the number of hungry people by 2015. But things were to get worse still. Four years later, at the UN Millennium Summit in September 2000, all that was actually proposed was that the "percentage" of the world's population suffering hunger should be halved by 2025. That presumably would mean very little less than 600 million people, instead of the 400 million promised in 1996.

It is likely that even this modest target will not be attained, if claimed necessary actions are not realized in time. According to the most recent facts available to FAO, the number of people suffering hunger in most of the developing countries increased "considerably" during the 1990s. It was only because successes were recorded in a few large Asian countries that the total number of undernourished people decreased at least by six million per year. If things go on at this rate, almost 700 million people will still be suffering hunger in 2015 – stricken by lack of carbohydrates, fat, protein, vitamins and minerals."

At the beginning of 2012, the new Director General of FAO announced that eradication of world hunger would be the goal until 2015. Well, it is a more than an ambitious objective, but nevertheless it is not ethical to respond: "Let's see, how many people we will have in 2015 suffering from hunger". It is an addressed challenge for all of us and everybody has to contribute to solve the problem and to safeguard the Human Rights Article 25 that all people living on earth can live in dignity and in peace.

In 2011/2012 more than one billion people are severely undernourished - this is an unacceptable tragedy!

Our first priority must be to create the technical basis for producing sufficient calories and energy-rich food to meet human needs throughout the world. We must bear in mind that over the next thirty to forty years world food requirements will more than double, and this will make it necessary to double - and even treble - agricultural production and supplies. At the same time, we will have to compensate for reduced farmland areas, water shortages and the switch from plant-based to meat-based diets. This not only requires a different sort of "green revolution", it also requires a "brown revolution" as well as a "blue revolution" in terms of soil and water conservation and sustainable use.

In the next thirty years we will have to produce more food worldwide than over the whole of the last 10,000 years. Beside this, today, water, soil and energy scarcities, hunger, and poverty remain prevalent throughout much of the developing world. If we are to live in a 21st century more prone to peace than violence, the developed countries must move expeditiously to address the developing countries' requirements for energy, water, and agricultural production. The availability, accessibility and affordability of energy, water and food supplies are vital to the economic development that is required to alleviate global poverty, to reduce global tensions, to reduce migration, to address global environmental degradation, and to open new markets for global goods and services.

Approaches / What MUST be done?

1. Place the focus on fighting poverty through increased productivity and purchasing power.
2. Give top priority again, after many years or even decades, to the development of agriculture and food production.
3. Focus on solutions for small-scale and large-scale farmers, and cooperatives.
4. Focus mainly on rural regions, though also on peri-urban areas.
5. Enable link-ups with value creation chains and networks.
6. Enable effective and efficient use of resources with regard to
   a. soil
   b. water
   c. nutrients
   d. crop plants
   e. biodiversity
   f. genetics
   g. carbon management
   h. human resources.
7. Endeavour to avoid changes in land use.
8. Establish fair, nationally and internationally legally binding regulations governing land and water rights for the protection of local populations, and arrange for necessary investments.
9. Set up agricultural production systems able to withstand climate change.
10. Drive the development of strategies to minimize greenhouse gases in agricultural production processes. This must include fostering of plant and animal production and the production of renewable raw materials (decentralized production of agro fuels).
11. Build up strategic warehouses/storage capacities in countries struggling against hunger, with capacity for sufficient reserves in the event of extreme harvest failures due to climatic conditions, and ensure ready availability (2010 Europe: wheat 5-year high, 144m tons).
12. Take steps to effect a significant reduction of harvest and food losses:
    a. pre- and post-harvest losses > 50%
    b. food production losses (production/distribution) > 60%.
13. Build up efficient national and regional agricultural research institutions in cooperation with the private sector and expand research and the transfer of technology.
14. Double Germany's research capacities in applied and development-oriented agriculture by 2015, with special emphasis on LDC nations.
15. Ensure that smallholders and farmers in LDC countries have free and unhindered access to modern agricultural inputs – especially in the case of women; freedom of choice must be respected.
16. Develop higher value crop plants (for preference through public activities) which are resistant to biotic and abiotic stress factors:
    a. tolerance to dryness, temperature, salt and ozone
    b. ICM pests, plant diseases and weeds
    c. building up of seed centres
    d. optimizing the photosynthetic efficiency of crop plants
    e. application of innovative technologies (epigenetics, …).
    The quality/genetic potential of locally available seed supplies is already now insufficient for resource-efficient production – with increasing climatic pressure this will become more problematic still by 2025/2050, most of all in Least Developed Countries.
17. Put an end to scientific apartheid in matters of "Green Gene Technology".

18. Set up technical agricultural training colleges and supraregional agricultural and nutritional competence centres (agro-marketing).
19. Protection against high price volatility:
    a. rapid information systems
    b. microcredits, insurances
    c. fair trade agreements
    d. own regional, national and international food stocks.
20. Draw up a time/financing plan: climate change and agriculture (2015/2020/2025):
    a. cf. Agenda 21/Rio+10 ... Rio+20 (United Nations, 1992, 2002, 2012)
    b. global action plan with set priorities (cf., e.g., Charter for Food Security, Maxwell, S., 1997)
    c. new, realistic targets: what can or must be done to react in time to the challenges, who must do this, and where?
21. Convene a "Round Table" with the private sector at CEO level and take up the initiative of the agri-food industry:
    a. all value chains/networks, combined forces of the agri-food, energy and biomass sectors
    b. early recognition and utilization of synergy potentials
    c. agreement on strategic cooperation clusters
22. Bring about an improvement in consumer behaviour in the industrial nations:
    a. reduction of "unethical" value attribution in the industrial nations with regard to staple food production
    b. throwing away of food by consumers (industrial countries: -30%) should to my mind be penalized in future
    c. quo vadis pet food? (booming markets/increasing consumption of resources).
23. Take steps to reduce dependence on fossil fuels throughout all stages of food and foodstuff production.
24. Tackle the new challenges for agriculture:
    a. do more with fewer resources and with better results – and do it in time!
    b. enhance efficiency and effectiveness in everything we do.
    c. dematerialization, decarbonization and reorganization of resources.
25. Start an immediate and sustained intensification in the production of staple foods and foodstuffs, with special focus on the developing countries/Least Developed Countries..
26. Lay down internationally binding regulations to prevent excessive speculation with agricultural commodity derivatives – adopt the proposals of the German Welthungerhilfe:
    a. create transparency on the commodity futures exchanges to identify the dealers in agricultural commodities – this market should be accessible only to distributors and retailers, not to financial speculators.
    b. impose limits on trading volumes.
    c. set upper limits for prices in order to prevent panic reactions and price distortions, which ultimately make hunger and poverty worse still and bring about social and political instability.
27. Ensure that the broadly based FFF Report ("The Future of Food and Farming: ...") from the Government Office for Science, London, UK (2011), with its solidly founded view on 2030 and 2050, is used in many countries as a basis for strategic action in order to achieve significant improvements in their efforts towards global food security, the fight against poverty and hunger, conservation of resources, and sustainable social development.

    This FFF Report should be compulsory reading for all decision makers, for schools, and ultimately for every one of us.

28. Engage further in objective dialogue (a core duty of journalists and media), but act immediately and in good time.
29. Urge people to develop a vision based on ethical considerations and at the same time to have the courage to put this vision into practice.
30. Make sure at all costs to prevent the food and oil prices from rising worldwide by 20-30% during the coming months.

Three equations written by Paul Collier in 2010 are landmarks for shaping the future in a sustainable way:

Nature + Technique + Rules = Prosperity,

Nature + Technique – Regulation = Plundering, and

Nature + Regulation – Technology = Hunger.

2044: "Overall, land use and land use changes have to be avoided as much as possible" (Burke, M. and Lobell, D., 2010).

"To acclimatize non-indigenous cereals in our regions, we must reproduce the conditions under which they thrive in their country of origin and as far as possible eliminate the factors which cause them to fail. At the same time we should not subject them to excessive artificial refinements, thereby turning them into weaklings attracting a host of diseases which we seldom observe in the wild growing plants." was claimed in Austria by Ignatz Magini in 1819.

2074: Vision: A global wake up call in 2012 and the implementation of shown actions will improve food security (availability, accessibility, affordability, acceptability) in order to go for Factor F^n: Future Farming, Food, Feed, Fitness, Fuel, Fiber, Flowers, Freshwater, Fishery, Forestry, Flora, Fauna, Fortune, Fun, Freedom, which are milestones on a roadmap for tackling the challenges of the 21st century.

Sustainable production of food, feed, fibre, fuel, freshwater and industrial products will depend for its success on a future-oriented, knowledge-based, resource-conserving, and added-value agriculture – that, finally, will eradicate hunger, enable freedom and safeguard global peace.

Concluding remarks:

Several future-oriented reports and recommendations for action have been drawn up since the publication of Agenda 21 in 1992. They are concerned mainly with describing the major goals which have to be achieved. Basically everything that needs to be done has been said, everything has been excellently described. The important thing, now more than ever, is to act immediately and more quickly than in 1992, knowing that the roads to be taken will be arduous and difficult.

Allow me to end on a hopeful note with the words of J. W. von Goethe: "To act is easy, to think is hard, to act as one thinks is the most difficult." We've done more than enough thinking, it's now 2012 and time to act!

A pdf of the exhibition "Visualized Agenda 21 / Rio+10 / Rio+20" (English, French, German, Portuguese, Spanish) is available on request.

Agenda 21 Rio + 20: Sustainable Development 2012

Source: Kern, M., 2011

Dr. Manfred Kern

ISSDA Göttingen 12/2011

agriEXCELLENCE

References:

Brandt, W.: Ansprache vor der UN-Vollversammlung, October, 1973, New York, 1973.

Burke, M. and Lobell, D.: Climate Change and Food Security: Adapting Agriculture to a Warmer World, Springer, New York, USA, 2010.

Cohen, J. E.: How Many People Can the Earth Support? W.W. Norton & Company, New York, London, 1995.

Collier, P.: The Plundered Planet - How to Reconcile Prosperity with Nature, Allen Lane an imprint of Penguin Books, London, 2010.

De Kruif, P.: Bezwinger des Hungers, Verlag 'Das Silberboot', Salzburg, 1928.

East, E.M.: Die Menschen am Scheideweg, Verlag Benno Schwabe & Co., Basel, 1926.

Greiling, W.: Wie werden wir leben? Ein Buch von den Aufgaben unserer Zeit, Econ Verlag, Düsseldorf, 1954.

Hooper, E.: Pakistan's Food Crisis – Water, Energy, Agriculture & Power: The Conflict Ahead, notes internationals CIDOB, 2010.

IFPRI (International Food Policy Research Institute), Concern Worldwide und Welthungerhilfe: Welthunger-Index 2010, Hungerforderung Hunger: Die Chance der ersten 1.000 Tage, Bonn, Washington, Dublin, 2010.

Kern, M.: Feeding the World: A Wider Perspective, Interview made by Sartorius, P., Future The Höchst Magazine 1/98, 24-28, 1998.

Kern, M.: Weltbevölkerungsentwicklung und Welternährung, Bundesakademie für Sicherheitspolitik in neuen Dimensionen, Kompendium zum erweiterten Sicherheitsbegriff, Verlag Mittler & Sohn, Hamburg, Berlin, Bonn, 501-526, 2001.

Kern, M.: Sicherung der Welternährung im 21. Jahrhundert – ein wesentlicher Beitrag zur Friedenssicherung, Vortrag auf der General-, Admiral- und Kommandeurtagung der Streitkräftebasis 2005, Führungsakademie der Bundeswehr in Hamburg, 2005.

Kern, M.: Clausewitz Gesellschaft e.V. 42. Sicherheitspolitische Informationstagung „Klimawandel – Energiesicherheit – Rohstoffe – Welternährung: Kardinalprobleme des 21. Jahrhunderts", FüAk Bundeswehr, Hamburg Europäische Sicherheit 12/2008, 76-79, 2008.

Kern, M.: Podiumsdiskussion: „Unser täglich Brot" Ernährungssicherheit trotz Klimawandel? 2. Ökumenischer Kirchentag 12.-16. Mai 2010, München, 2010.

Kern, M.: Land Resources and Land Use Options – Challenges for Food Security to Climate Change, In: Proceedings 2nd IFSDAA-Meeting, Crop Science and Land Use for Food and Bioenergy. (eds.) Behl, R.K., Merbach, W., Meliczek, H. and Kaetsch, Ch. (eds.), Agrobios International, India, 2010.

Kern, M.: Public Hearing on the subject of "Global Nutrition", 35th Session of the Committee on Food, Agriculture and Consumer Protection of the German Bundestag, 17th Legislative Period, April 4th, 2011, Berlin, 2011.

Kern, M.: Food Security at the Crossroads Anno 1864, 1894, 1924, 1954, 1984, 2014, 2044, 2074 - A Wake up Call! - Plenary lecture given during the International Seminar on "Sustainable Land Use and the Food Chain" of ISSDA (International Society for Sustainable Development and Agriculture, December 1-3, 2011, Göttingen, Germany, 2011.

Lord John Boyd Orr, Nobel Laureate in: Borlaug, N.: Nobel Lecture, December 11, 1970 "The Green Revolution, Peace, and Humanity", Nobelprize.org , 1970.

Magini, I.: Ueber den Anbau der Getreidearten – Ein Beitrag zur Lösung der Frage: "Welche fremde Getreidearten sind einer besonderen Aufmerksamkeit und Cultur würdig?" Im Verlage Leopold Grund, Wien, Austria, 1819.

Maxwell, S.: A Charter for Food Security, Food Policy 22/6, 469-473, 1997.

Murphy, W.B. (ed.): The future world of agriculture, Walt Disney World EPCOT Center book, USA, 1984.

Pracht, H.-P.: Abschied von der Heimat, Die Eifeler Auswanderung nach Amerika im 19. Jahrhundert, Helios Verlag, Aachen, 1998.

Research Councils UK: Global Food Security, Strategic Plan 2011-2016, Research Councils UK, international service provider, 2011.

Rosenblum, J.W.: Agriculture in the Twenty-First Century, John Wiley & Sons, 1983.

Schwerdt, H.: The Source of Gold or The Farmer on the Path of Progress – A Narrative for the Common Folk as a Contribution to Promoting an Agriculture in Keeping with our Times, 1859.

The Government Office for Science, London, UK: Foresight. The Future of Food and Farming 2010, Challenges and choises for global sustainability, Final Project Report, London 2011.

The Government Office for Science, London, UK: Foresight. The Future of Food and Farming 2010, Challenges and choises for global sustainability, Action Plan, London, 2011.

Tsakok, I.: Success in Agricultural Transformation – What It Means and What Makes It Happen, Cambridge University Press, Cambridge, 2011.

United Nations: The Universal Declaration of Human Rights, Vienna, http://www.un.org/en/documents/udhr, 1948.

United Nations: Earth Summit Agenda 21, Rio de Janeiro, http://www.un.org/esa/dsd/agenda21/res agenda21 00.shtml, 1992.

Walt Disney World: The Future World of Agriculture, 1984.

Further reading:

Coff, Ch.: The Taste for Ethics – An Ethic of Food Consumption, Springer, The Netherlands, 2006.

Cohen, J.E.: How Many People Can the Earth Support? W.W. Norton & Company, New York, London, 1995.

Falvey, L.: Religion and Agriculture, Sustainability in Christianity and Buddhism, Institute for International Development, Adelaide, Australia, 2005.

Juma, C.: The New Harvest – Agricultural Innovation in Africa, Oxford University Press, 2011.

Kern, M.: Future of Agriculture, Global Dialogue EXPO 2000: The Role of the Village in the 21st Century: Crops, Jobs and Livelihood, 15-17 August 2000, Hanover, Germany, Aventis CropScience, Germany, 2000.

Koerner, L.: Linnaeus Nature and Nation, Harvard University Press, Cambridge, London, 1999.

OECD Trade and Agriculture Directorate / Environment Directorate: Joint Working Party on Agriculture and the Environment, Climate Change and Agriculture: Impacts, Adaptation and Mitigation, Brussels, 2010.

Schägerl, Ch.: Menschenzeit – Zerstören oder gestalten – Die entscheidende Epoche unseres Planten, Riemann Verlag, München, 2010.

Smith, B. D.: The Emergence of Agriculture, Scientific American Library, New York, 1995.

Spedding, C. R. W.: Agriculture and the Citizen, Chapman & Hall, Oxford, 1996.

Tainter, J. A.: The Collapse of Complex Societies, Cambridge University Press, 1988.

Tertzakian, P.: A Thousand Barrels a Second, The Coming Oil Break Point and the Challenges Facing an Energy Dependent World, McGraw-Hill, New York, 2007.

Timner, C. P.: A World without Agriculture? The Historical Paradox of Agricultural Development, American Enterprise Institute for Public Policy Research, 1/May 2009, Washington, 2009.

UNESCO: Science Report 2010, Ein aktuelles Bild der Wissenschaft weltweit, Deutsche UNESCO-Kommission e.V., Bonn, 2010.

UNDP-Report 2001: Making new technologies work for human development", UNDP-Report 2001, Oxford University Press, New York, Oxford, 2001.

Verlautbarungen des Apostolischen Stuhls: Enzyklica CARITAS IN VERITATE von Papst Benedikt XVI. An die Bischöfe, an die Priester und Diakone, an die Personen gottgeweihten Lebens, an die christgläubigen Laien und alle Menschen guten Willens über die ganzheitliche Entwicklung des Menschen in der Liebe und in der Wahrheit, Verlautbarungen des Apostolischen Stuhls Nr. 186, Rom, 29. Juni 2009.

W.I.R.E.: Money Is Dead. Long Live Money. On the Change in Currencies and Values, Abstract No. 2/2011, W.I.R.E., Think Tank of Bank Sarasin % Co. Ltd. And the Collegium Helveticum of the Federal Institute of Technology (ETH) and the University of Zurich, Switzerland, 2011.

World Bank: World Development Report 2008, Agriculture for Development, The World   Bank, Washington, USA, 2008.

World Economic Forum Davos: From Risk to Opportunity: Building a Response to the New Reality. Outlook on the Global Agenda 2011, World Economic Forum, Geneva, 2011.

Emerging Technologies for Sustainable Wheat Production Management and Genetic Options

Ashok Kumar, Ashok Yadav, S.K.Sethi[1], K.D.Sharma , S.K. Thakral and R.K.Behl[1]*

Department of Agronomy, [1]Department of Genetics and Plant Breeding, CCS Haryana Agriculture University, Hisar-125004 (Haryana) India
*Presenting author: 338 Sector 15A, Hisar-125001 (Haryana), India

ABSTRACT

India has witnessed a significant increase in wheat production after the green revolution. However, the green revolution was confined to Indo-Gangetic Plains which contributed more than 70 percent of the total wheat production. This was mainly due to increased productivity of dwarf plant types responsive to high inputs. The gap between the attained and attainable yield is large. Therefore, significant scope exists for yield improvement in Indo-Gangetic Plains as well as in other wheat growing zones by breaking yield barriers through genetic enhancement and by adopting new cost effective and sustainable technologies. The time has come to adopt an integrated approach towards development of technologies for resource conservation, sustainable water soil health, increased yield and profitability. Exploitation of heterosis through hybrids provides an opportunity after the demonstration of male sterility. Zero tillage and furrow irrigated raised bed systems will solve many agronomic problems along with economization of wheat production. The use of bio-inoculants like VAM helps in increasing fertilizer and water use efficiency and grain yield and its quality. Seed priming is becoming popular among farmers, especially in late planting situations which are common in rice-wheat system. Relay cropping of summer green gram in the standing wheat crop has shown promising results in rice-wheat cropping systems by restoring soil fertility and augmenting farmer's income.

Introduction

Wheat (Triticum spp.) is the second most important cereal after rice in India. Bread wheat *(T. aestivum)* contributes approximately 86 percent, durum wheat about 12 percent and dicoccum only 2 percent of the total production. *T. aestivum* is grown in almost all wheat growing areas whereas *T. durum* in central and southern parts of India and *T. dicoccum* in Karnataka and southern Maharashtra. Wheat provides more than 50 percent of the calories to the people who mainly depend on it thus contributing substantially to national food security. India will require 109 million tons (mt) of wheat by 2020 with a growth rate of approximately 3 percent per annum to feed its population of about 1.3 billion people. However, the wheat production was 81 mt in 2009-10 with a growth rate of 2.2 percent per annum from 1986-87 (Singh, 2010).

In India, wheat production has increased 13 times from 6.4 mt in 1950 to 85.93 mt in 2011. There has been a significant achievement towards the target of 100 mt by 2030 for ensured food security (Anonymous, 2011). However, to meet the food security 1.5 mt of additional wheat per year would be required. Such a daunting task may not be achieved easily considering the various natural and technological constraints. Today wheat plays an increasingly important role in the management of India's food economy and in food grain production it accounts for 35 percent.

Wheat Growing Zones

In India, wheat is grown in an area of about 28 million ha and the cultivation extends from a latitude of 9 degrees North (Palni hills) to above 35 degrees North (Srinagar valley of Jammu and Kashmir). Considering the exposure of wheat to a wide range of agro-climatic changes such as humidity, temperature, photoperiod, soil type, altitude and latitude, India is divided in to six zones for wheat production (Table 1).

About 91.5 percent of the wheat is produced in six states viz. Uttar Pradesh, Punjab, Haryana, Madhya Pradesh, Rajasthan and Bihar. Uttar Pradesh with 24.3 mt is the highest producer of wheat followed by Punjab (14.7 mt) and Haryana (9.1 mt). The contribution from Haryana and Punjab is due to high productivity (4.0 to 4.3 tons/ha) while the contribution of Uttar Pradesh and Madhya Pradesh is due to a relatively large area (50 percent of the total area) sown to wheat.

Table 1: Approximate area and states covered for wheat cultivation in six zones.

Zone	States covered	Area (2007-08)	
		M ha	%
North Hill Zone (NHZ)	Western Himalayan regions of J & K (except Jammu and Kathua distt.), Himachal Pardesh (except Una and Paonta Valley), Uttarnchal (except Tarai area), Sikkim and hills of West Bengal and North Eastern States	0.8	2.9
North Western Plain Zone (NWPZ)	Punjab, Haryana, Delhi, Rajasthan (except Kota and Udaipur divisions), Western Uttar Pradesh (except Jhansi division), Jammu and Kathua distt. of J & K, Una and Paonta Valley of Himachal Pradesh and Tarai region of Uttaranchal	11.1	40.1
North Eastern Plain Zone (NEPZ)	Eastern Uttar Pradesh, Bihar, Jharkhand, Orissa, West Bangal, Assam and Plains of North Eastern States	9.2	33.2
Central Zone (CZ)	Madhya Pradesh, Chhattisgarh, Gujarat, Kota and Udaipur divisions of Rajasthan, Jhansi division of Uttar Pradesh	5.0	18.1
Peninsular Zone (PZ)	Maharashtra, Karnataka, Andhra Pradesh, Goa, Plains of Tamil Nadu	1.5	5.4
Southern Hill Zone (SHZ)	Hilly areas of Tamil Nadu and Kerala comprising of the Nilgiri and Palni hills	0.1	0.4
Total		27.7	100.0

Wheat Growing Seasons

In India, wheat is cultivated from mid-October to April, i.e., during winter season except in hills of North India where the season extends to May. The optimum average day night temperature is 23 °C. The crop experiences cold months of December and January followed by warmer months of March and April. The variable growing period in different ago-climatic zones causes differences in length of each phenophase, especially grain filling which lead to differences in attainable yield. Wheat growing duration is maximum in NHZ and minimum in PZ. Nearly, 89 percent of wheat is grown as irrigated and most of it lies in Northern states. In the central, peninsular and hilly areas of Gujarat, Madhya Pradesh, Karnataka and Maharashtra, the crop is mostly grown as rain fed on conserved soil moisture during the monsoon rains. In these areas, restricted irrigation is also becoming popular.

Zonal Production Constraints

Recent studies show a climatic yield gap-I (difference between climatic potential yields and district average yields) as 33 percent and a management yield gap-II (difference between of experimental plot yields to district average yields) as 16 percent in wheat. The major constraints in wheat production in high productivity zone of NWPZ are deteriorating soil health, falling water tables, water logging, soil salinity, drought and terminal high temperature stresses, infestation of karnal bunt, leaf rust and weeds. Abiotic stresses such as drought and high temperature and diseases like leaf and stem rusts, and leaf blight are also common in central and peninsular zones. Water logging and micro-nutrient deficiency have become common in NWPZ and EZ. Other factors such as timely availability of quality seeds, fertilizer and mechanization are more common in NEPZ, CZ and PZ. Some of the states also lack in good extension facilities.

The average productivity of wheat in high productivity zones, NWPZ and NEPZ is constant or even declining since last decade. As a result, India has to import wheat, which otherwise was available in surplus quantities. The main reason for this are delayed sowing of wheat due to late harvesting of scented rice, endemic infestation of *Phalaris minor*, degrading soil health due to excessive mining of soil resulting into micro-nutrient deficiency, falling water table, etc. The crop in these areas encounters terminal drought and high temperature stress, which causes drastic yield reductions.

Low Cost Technologies for Sustainable Production

The falling wheat productivity can be tackled on two fronts, i.e., on the crop improvement and the crop production front. On the crop improvement front, the yield barriers can be broken by exploitation of heterosis for development of hybrids, hybridization of winter and spring wheats, development of synthetic wheats, use of buitre, Chinese germplasm and alien species. Biotechnological interventions such as structural and functional genomics, gene pyramiding, marker assisted selection for abiotic, biotic and quality traits may be promising.

On the production front, management of abiotic stresses such as drought, salt, water logging and terminal high temperature require concerted attention. Inevitably, the wheat productivity is likely to become critical with changing climatic scenarios if urgent actions are not taken to prepare farmers to adapt soil and crop management practice appropriate to resource constraints and changing climatic scenarios. It is a fact that each 1°C rise in temperature will increase the demand for irrigation water to sustain production at the current levels. Thus, wheat productivity in all growing zones especially in NWPZ, NEPZ and CZ has to depend mainly on improved resource base, crop diversification and input use efficiency under normal and problematic soils and water conditions.

Significant efforts have been made through on-station and farmers participatory research to develop customized solutions to address the issues of natural resource fatigue, declining water tables, decelerating factor productivity, terminal heat stress and shrinking farm profitability. The plants exposed to high temperatures and water stress influence the plant water status which in turn adversely affects the physiological traits. This could help in identifying the suitability of cultivars for different sowing dates and irrigation levels, and the traits to screen for water and heat stress (Kumar and Singh, 2001, Kumar et al., 2008, 2009, Sharma and Kumar, 2010 a, b; Table 2).

Higher canopy temperature depression and tissue water content in wheat resulted in lower cell membrane injury (low electrolyte leakage) and were positively related to grain yield (Kumar et al., 2008, Sharma and Kumar, 2009; Table 3). The effect of drought and high temperature stress can be moderated by AM inoculation under timely and late sown crop. The mycorrhizal application improved yield attributes, yields and grain quality, and the effect was compounded when fungal inoculation was preceded by seed priming (soaking of seed overnight in water) (Kumar et al., 2011; Table 4). The protein content and wet gluten in the grains was improved significantly with fungi inoculation.

Conservation agriculture based resource conservation technologies have proved to produce more at less costs, reduce environmental pollution, promote conjunctive use of organics (avoids residue burning), improve soil health and promotes timely planting of winter crops to address issues of terminal heat stresses in the region such as zero tillage wheat. Results of multi-location trials, conducted in farmer fields by CCS HAU showed that wheat yields were relatively more in zero till than the conventional tilled practice (Fig. 1).

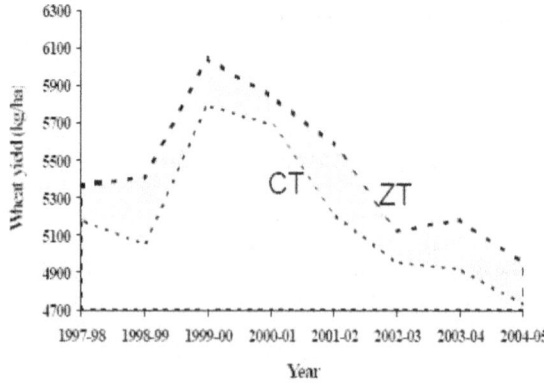

Fig. 1 Wheat yield under conventional tillage (CT) and zero till (ZT) in Haryana.

Table 2. Physiological traits influenced by sowing time, irrigation and cultivars

Treatment	Canopy temperature depression (°C)		Tissue water content		Cell membrane injury (%)	
	Before KI spray	7d after KI spray	Before KI spray	7d after KI spray	Before KI spray	7d after KI spray
Date of sowing						
21 Nov.	7.84	3.20	0.83	0.79	4.97	8.31
22 Dec.	4.32	2.97	0.78	0.73	9.92	17.72
CD (5%)	0.11	0.17	0.02	0.01	0.21	0.21
Irrigation levels						
Irrigated (I_N)	5.84	5.42	0.82	0.80	7.26	7.78
I_N+KI	5.86	0.70	0.81	0.71	7.31	28.0
I_0	3.32	2.97	0.78	0.72	9.64	10.75
CD (5%)	0.11	0.20	0.02	0.05	0.21	0.25
Genotypes						
NIAW 34	4.38	2.96	0.81	0.77	8.40	15.88
PBW 343	5.00	3.35	0.80	0.76	7.60	11.78
Raj 3765	4.92	3.37	0.79	0.75	8.60	16.41
WH 711	4.03	2.45	0.80	0.75	9.20	18.00
CD (5%)	0.30	0.23	0.01	0.09	0.16	0.26

I_N= Irrigated, KI= Potassium iodide spray (0.2% conc.), I_0= No post sowing irrigation

Table 3. Correlation matrix of traits measured on 17 genotypes in drought environment

Traits	LWP	RWC	E	P_N	CTD
RWC	-0.89**				
E	-0.31	0.60*			
P_N	-0.31	0.45	0.78*		
CTD	0.47	-0.76**	-	-0.65**	
Water use	-0.60*	0.62*	0.50*	0.45	0.58*
Spikes/ m²	-0.33	0.59*	0.65*	0.39	-0.79**
Grains/ spike	-0.37	0.66**	0.57*	0.55*	-0.60*
Seed size	-0.50*	0.36	-0.13	0.02	0.02
Harvest index	-0.13	0.40	0.33	0.12	-0.46
Biomass	-0.46	0.66**	0.83*	0.71**	-0.81**
Seed yield	-0.45	0.78**	0.89*	0.67**	-0.95**

LWP: leaf water potential, RWC: leaf relative water content, E: transpiration rate, P_N: photosynthesis, CTD: canopy temperature depression, HI: harvest index, *P<0.05, **P<0.01

Table 4. Yields of two wheat varieties as influenced by different treatments

Treatments	'PBW 343'		'WH 1021'	
	Biomass (kg/ha)	Grain yield (kg/ha)	Biomass (kg/ha)	Grain yield (kg/ha)
Dry seed (DS)	15696.6	5168.6	9100.5	3921.7
Primed seed (PS)	18871.2	5752.0	10652.5	4483.9
DS + AM	17989.4	5337.9	9947.0	4005.6
PS + AM	19223.9	6507.2	11111.1	4672.6
CD (P=0.01)	1295.6	743.40	899.43	443.6
CV (%)	4.17	7.67	5.17	6.17

But the terminal heat and climate changes did adversely affect wheat yield since 1999-2000. Now, it has been realized that due to delayed wheat sowing, the crop suffers from high temperature during the months of March and April, which adversely affect the yield. CCS Haryana Agricultural University along with the Department of Agriculture, Haryana State has launched an awareness campaign for timely sowing as well as seed priming (2007-09), which resulted into significant yield gains in timely and delayed planted wheat (Table 5). Yield gains of 656 and 960 kg/ha, respectively under late and timely sowing were recorded mainly due to good germination, early plant vigour and higher tillering. On an average, grain yield of wheat was increased by 5-11.6 percent due to seed priming on farmers' field. In wheat, good germination, early plant vigour, higher tillering and grain yield can be obtained by seed priming. A decline in yield of 0.7 to 1.5 percent per day of delay in wheat sowing is common, which may be compensated by early germination of primed seed. Late and poor emergence under low temperature and hardening soils and coincidence of terminal high temperature and drought stress are major obstacles in late planted crop.

Table 5. Grain yield of wheat sown on 20-25 December (Experimental station, Hisar)

Treatment	Grain yield (kg/ha)			
	2004-05	2005-06	2006-07	Mean
Primed seed	5487	5600	4678	5255
Unprimed seed	5243	5044	4084	4790
CD (5%)	176	205	223	

In addition, resource conservation technology, bed-planting has both a yield as well as an economic advantage (Kumar et al., 2005, Kumar et al., 2010). The Modified FIRBS technology consists of seeding 3 rows on raised beds (60 cm wide) with 20 cm spacing between the rows. Bed height is normally 18-20 cm. Irrigation water is applied to the corrugations between the beds as shown in Fig. 2. Water saving by modified FIRBS ranged from 10 to 66.9

percent from 1st to 5th irrigation with an average of 41.4 percent and significantly higher water productivity over the flat planting. Higher leaf area, photosynthetic rates, number of grains/spike and biomass led to higher grain yield of wheat in modified FIRBS than flat planting. In timely sown wheat, abrupt rise in temperature in March coincide with grain filling, thus resulting in to forced maturity, shriveled and decreased number of grains and finally the grain yield.

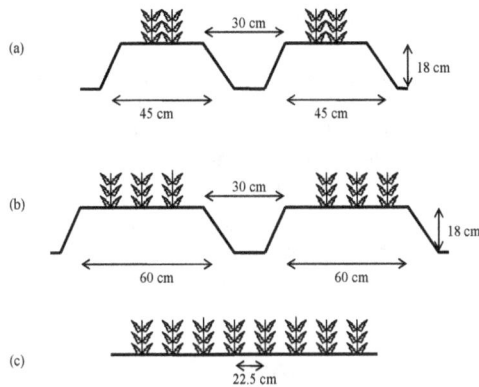

Fig. 2 Patterns of (a)-Traditional FIRBS, (b)-Modified FIRBS and (c)-Flat sowing

These yield reductions may be avoided by application of irrigation at grain filling and subsequent relay cropping of summer green gram. The practice is more suited and economical under modified FIRBS, where 2 rows of green gram are planted between 3 rows of wheat on the beds. This will have twin benefit of doubling farm profitability by green gram, and reduce NO$_3$-N pollution of ground water aquifers which is leached out during monsoon season.

To increase water productivity in irrigated wheat, the laser assisted precision land levelling has revealed that on an average 30 percent of irrigation water and 17 percent yield gains can be achieved with other benefits of saving in time of operations of farm machinery, and increase in area under plow due to removal of bunds and channels (post levelling increased plot size for irrigation) in rice-wheat systems.

Hybrid Wheat

Hybrid wheat is one of the approaches to overcome the yield plateau. Hybrid seed can be produced using either a cytoplasmic-genetic male sterility restorer system (CGMS) or by using chemical hybridizing agents (CHAs). A requirement of any method of obtaining male sterility in wheat is the control of pollen production in all florets including those produced by early or late tillers (Pickett, 1993). The CGMS system besides being time consuming has the limitation of finding out not only the maintainers but also the complete fertility restorers in wheat. The induction of male sterility in wheat by CHAs or gametocides is a potentially attractive and rapid method to develop female parents for hybrid seed production. The primary advantage of CHA's is that no fertility restoration system or separate maintenance of the male sterile line is required as in the CGMS system and this saves time, labour and money needed for transferring male sterility. Compared with CMS system, an effective CHA allows the production of large number of parental combinations and permits the evaluation of a number of inbreeds for combining ability and /or breeding value.

Commercial Status of Hybrid Wheat

The first wheat variety using male sterility restoration system was released in 1978 in USA by De Kalb and Pioneer. Similarly, RH01 (Frandoc x Festin) was the first commercial hybrid extensively tested in Italy. Bruns and Peterson (1998) reported that hybrid wheat in the great plains of the USA has shown a fundamental yield responsiveness and selection gain advantage over pure line varieties that could result in acceptance by producers.

The Maharashtra Hybrid Seed Company (MAHYCO) in collaboration with Monsanto of U.S.A. is the only company, which has commercialized hybrid wheat in India. Two CMS based hybrid cultivars: Pratham 7070 and Pratham 7050 have been released for Eastern, Central and Peninsular Zones of India.

Chemical Hybridizing Agents (CHAs)

Chemical hybridizing agents (CHAs) have been proposed to induce functional male sterility. The use of CHAs in crop breeding has now attained noticeable success in rice and wheat in China and USA, respectively. Using the CHA approach, sufficiently large quantity of hybrid seed is being produced in France, Italy and USA which are way ahead in commercializing wheat hybrids. Their success indicated that CHA is a powerful tool to create new hybrid varieties. Sethi and Gill (2003) also advocated that CHAs can facilitate onset of male sterility and mimic genetic systems for production of hybrids.

The observation of complete pollen sterility on plants treated with maleic hydrazide by Chopra *et al.* (1960) opened the first door towards the possible use of CHAs for hybrid seed production in wheat. Later, several companies like Rohm and Haas, Shell and Monsanto have carried out extensive work on development of gametocides (Knudson and Ruttan, 1988). Sethi *et al.* (1998a, 1998b) also reported that more than 1000 ppm of Etheral should be sprayed on wheat to achieve sufficient level of male sterility. Now a days, two major chemical molecules are used commercially to produce hybrid seed: (1) Genesis, developed by Monsanto, U.S.A. and (2) Croisor produced by Hybrinova, France (Blouet *et al.*, 1999).

The expression and duration of CHA induced male sterility is very stage specific and vulnerable to prevailing environmental conditions. A serious reduction in seed purity can result from incomplete male sterility and might cause seed certification problems. The key points for successful CHA hybrid seed production are effective chemically induced emasculation to guarantee the purity of hybrid seed and promotion of cross pollination to get more of hybrid seed.

Sethi and Gill (2004) found significant differences between the four varieties sprayed with eighteen CHAs for male and female sterility. UP 2425 exhibited the highest male sterility and PBW 343 was found to be more sensitive owing to damage to its female reproductive parts. WH 542 showed least response for induction of male sterility.

Cytoplasmic Genetic Male Sterility System (CGMS)

The availability of stable cytoplasmic male sterile lines and effective restorers is an essential pre-requisite for a hybrid wheat breeding programme. However, significant effect of cytoplasm on some traits in positive or negative direction has been observed. Cytoplasmic x nuclear interaction effects have also been reported for successful hybrid wheat breeding programme. Studies on cytoplasmic sources and their interaction with different nuclear background are needed.

Pickett (1993) reported 20 different cytoplasms from *Aegilops*, one each from *Haynaldia* and *Secale*, and five cytoplasms from the genus *Triticum*. He concluded that CMS derived from *Triticum* appeared to present fewer problems and pointed to the moderately successful commercialization of hybrids produced with the *T. timopheevii* CMS system in the United States. He *et al.* (1996) working for Chinese national hybrid wheat network first emphasized the use of *T. timopheevii* CMS, but that *Ae. kotschyi* and *Ae. ventricosa* were also being utilized. They report that three hybrids based on *T. timopheevii* and six hybrids based on *Ae. kotschyi* had a 15 percent advantage over commercial pure line cultivars. Sethi and Ashwani (2010) also observed that CMS lines flowered late as compared to maintainer lines, under late sown conditions. Differences in out crossing potential are reflected by the seed set on the CMS lines. This trait is largely affected by glumes opening angle. Lines with larger glumes opening angle showed higher seed set and lines showed reduction in seed set under late sown conditions. These findings are supported by the studies of Chauhan (2000) , Tomar and Anblagan (2004) , and Rana et al. (2007, 2008).

Heterosis for Grain Yield

Pickett (1993) reviewed heterosis in winter wheat. Maximum high-parent heterosis ranged from 24.7 to 76.0 percent among the hybrids (based on reports published between 1931 and 1982) and from 9.4 to 160.4 percent (1938-1986). Grain yield is clearly the economic trait of interest in hybrid wheat. However, Pickett (1993) also laid emphasis on other components as grain number, grain weight and tillering as a principal source of heterosis. Thirty two percent yield advantages over the existing hybrids have been reported (Srivastava *et al.*, 1998). Sethi and Gill (2003) reported standard heterosis ranging from 11.72 to 20.68 percent among the hybrids HWH 21, HWH 26, HWH 30 and HWH 47.

Hybrid Wheat Seed Production

Seed production is a vital part of any hybrid programme. The percent seed set on a male sterile plant forms an important economic factor in seed production. For successful adoption of 'hybrid variety' technology, the essential prerequisites are the availability of a proper pollination control system to enable production of commercial quantities of hybrid seed, and the existence of adequate degree of heterosis to make the hybrid commercial viable (Poeh-lman and Sleeper, 1995).

With the advent of discovery of CMS in wheat breeders were encouraged to expand considerable effort in research on F_1 hybrids (Pickett, 1993; Jordaan, 1996). Hybrid seed production in wheat using CMS is a three lines system and involves three steps (Virmani and Edwards, 1983): (1) Multiplication of CMS (A-lines); (2) Multiplication of maintainer (B) and restorer R-lines; and (3) Production of hybrid seed (AxR). In using the chemical system to produce hybrids, two lines would be necessary, a P- line (pollinator) for use as the male parent and C- line (chemical male sterile) used as the female parent (Rowell and Miller, 1971). The effective use and versatility of CHAs will depend on genotype-chemical, environment-chemical, and genotype-environment-chemical interactions (Virmani and Edwards, 1983). As the success of hybrid wheat depends greatly on the female seed production, cross-pollination of sufficient magnitude and reliability is essential to the economic production of hybrid seed.

Hybrid Wheat Economics

The successful adoption of any hybrid crop requires that a certain level of economic profitability be met. Hybrid seed costs more than certified varietal seed or farmer-saved seed. The economic threshold for the acceptance of hybrid wheat is a complex function of a number of factors beyond the additional quantity of grain produced by the hybrid. These factors include: a) Hybrid advantage, such as yield stability, pest protection and agronomic traits important in any specific hybrid versus cultivar comparison; b) Average purchase price of hybrid seed versus varietal seed; c) Anticipated commodity price of grain, or other market factors; d) Expected return on the hybrid seed investment by the grower; e) Seeding rate of the hybrid versus the cultivar and f) Risk of crop failure due to natural disasters.

References:

Anonymous: Progress report of the All India Coordinated Wheat & Barley improvement Project 2010-11 – Project Director's Report. (Ed.) Indu Sharma, DWR, Karnal (Haryana), 74, 2011.

Blouet, A., Streiff, K. and Guckert, A.: Possibilities for hybrid seed production in wheat. **In**: Heterosis and hybrid seed production in agronomic crops. Barsa, A.S. (Ed.), The Haworth Press Inc., U.S.A. , 81-117, 1999.

Bruns, R. and Peterson, C. J.: Yield and stability factors associated with hybrid wheat. *Euphytica*, 100, 1-5, 1998.

Chauhan, A. K.: Studies on maintenance and restoration of cytoplasmic genic male sterile lines of wheat (*Triticum aestivum* L.). M.Sc. Thesis, CCS Haryana Agricultural University, Hisar, 2000.

Chopra, V. L., Jain, S. K. and Swaminathan, M.S.: Studies on chemical induction of pollen sterility in some crop plants. *Indian J. Genet.* 20, 188-199, 1960.

He, Z. E., Du, Z.E and Zuang, Q. S.: Progress of wheat breeding research in China. International Wheat Conference, Ankara, Turkey, 32-33, 1996.

Jordaan, J. P.: Hybrid wheat: Advances and challenges. In: Increasing yield potential in wheat: Breaking the barriers, Renolods, M.P. and McNab, A., (Eds.) CIMMYT, Mexico DF, 1996.

Knudson, M. K. and Ruttan, V. W.: Research and development of a biological innovation: commercial hybrid wheat. *Food Res. Inst. Study.* 21, 45-68, 1988.

Kumar, A., Bali, Y., Sharma, K. D. and Thakral, S. K.: Evaluation of wheat genotypes for terminal heat tolerance by simple physiological traits. Indian Journal of Plant Physiology 13 (1) , 39-43, 2008.

Kumar, A, Sharma, K.D. and Behl, R. K.: Using root characteristics as selection criteria in breeding for drought tolerance. In: Genetic Enhancement in Field Crops for Input Use Efficiency and Tolerance to Abiotic Stresses. (R.K. Behl, S.K. Sethi, A.K. Chhabra, D. Singh, S.S. Dhanda, Eds.), Winter School (October 15 to November 4, 2009), Department of Plant Breeding, CCS Haryana Agricultural University, Hisar, 300-305, 2009.

Kumar, A., Sharma, K. D. and Gera, R.: Arbuscular mycorrhizae (*Glomus mosseae*) symbiosis for increasing the yield and quality of wheat (*Triticum aestivum*). Indian Journal of Agricultural Sciences 81 (5), 478-480, 2011.

Kumar. A., Sharma, K.D. and Yadav, A. Enhancing yield and water productivity of wheat through furrow irrigated raised bed system in Indo-Gangetic Plains of India. Indian Journal of Agricultural Sciences 80 (3) 198-202, 2010.

Kumar, A. and Singh, D.P.: Screening of wheat and chickpea genotypes for seed yield by infrared thermometer under field conditions. Haryana Journal of Agronomy 17 (1,2), 1-8, 2001.

Kumar, M., Yadav, A., Malik. R.K., Kumar, A., Yadav, M. and Singh, S.: Impact of methods and time of nitrogen application on the performance of wheat planted on raised beds. Project Workshop Proceedings (June 1-2, 2005), Accelerating the Adoption of Resource Conservation Technologies in Rice-Wheat Systems of the Indo-Gangetic Plants (Eds. R.K. Malik, R.K. Gupta, C.M. Singh, A. Yadav, S.S. Brar, T.C. Thakur, S.S. Singh, A.K. Singh, R. Singh, R.K. Sinha), Directorate of Extension Education, CCS Haryana Agricultural University, Hisar, 87-90, 2005.

Pickett, A. A.: Hybrid wheat – results and problems. *Adv. Pl. Breed,* 15, 259, 1993.

Poehlman, J. M. and Sleeper, D. A.: Breeding field crops. 4th ed. (Indian print) Panima Publishing Corporation, New Delhi, 1995.

Rana Jyoti, Sethi, S. K. and Behl, R. K.: Characterization of cytoplasmic male sterile lines in wheat (*Triticum aestivum* L.). *Agri. Bio Research 12 (2), 139-144*, 2007.

Rana Jyoti, Sethi, S. K. and Behl, R. K.: Characterization of cytoplasmic male sterile lines in wheat (*Triticum aestivum* L.) on the basis of floral traits. *Annals of Biology.* 24(1), 41-45, 2008.

Rowell, P. L. and Miller, D. G.: Induction of male sterility in wheat with 2-chloroethyle phosphonic acid (Etheral). *Crop Sci., 11,* 629-631, 1971.

Sethi, S. K. and Kumar, A.: Hybrid wheat: Developmental approaches and impact analysis, In: Crop Science and Land Use for Food and Bioenergy (Eds: Behl, R. K., Merbach, W., Meliczek, H. and Kaetsch, C.) Agrobios International, Jodhpur, 35-50, 2010.

Sethi, S. K. and Gill, H. S.: Hybrid wheat innovative approach for food security. In: Enhancing production and food values of plants: Genetic options. (eds.) Behl, R.K. and Chhabra, A.K., SSARM, CCS HAU, Hisar. 1, 121-125, 2003.

Sethi, S. K. and Gill, H. S.: Wheat varieties vis-à-vis chemical hybridizing agents. Paper presented in 91st Indian Science Congress held in Punjab University, Chandigarh, Jan. 3-7, 2004, Abst. III: 59, 2004.

Sethi, S. K., Gill, H. S. and Rana, R. K.: Performance of wheat hybrids produced through Chemical hybridizing agent. Paper presented in National Seminar on advances In Genetics and Plant Breeding-Impact of DNA Revolution, UAS, Dharwad, Oct. 30-31, Abst., 128, 2003.

Sethi, S. K., Srivastava, R. B. and Singh, D.: Introduction of male sterility with CHAs in wheat for the exploitation of heterosis. Paper presented in Seminar on Heterosis- Its Commercial Exploitation COA, Nagpur, March 10-11, 1998. Abst. , 17-18, 1998a.

Sethi, S. K., Srivastava, R. B. and Yunus, M.: Efficacy of chemical hybridizing agents for induction of male sterility in wheat. Paper presented in International Conference on Food Security and Crop Science Hisar, Nov. 3-6, 1998, Abst., 102-103, 1998b.

Sharma, K. D. and Kumar, A.: Physiological processes associated with grain yield of wheat (*Triticum aestivum* L.) under restricted soil moisture. Indian Journal of Plant Physiology 14 (1), 55-59, 2009.

Sharma K. D. and Kumar, A.: Physiological and management approaches to mitigate terminal high temperature stress in wheat (Triticum aestivum L.). J. Agrometeorology 11, 57-60, 2010a.

Sharma K. D. and Kumar, A.: Genotypic variation for agro-physiological traits and their utilization as screening techniques for drought tolerance in wheat. Indian Journal of Genetics & Plant Breeding 70 (1), 1-5, 2010b.

Singh, S. S.: Wheat scenario in India- Transition from the green revolution to the present. Indian Farming 60 (5), 4-11, 2010.

Srivastava, R. B., Singh, V. P. and Sethi, S.K.: Problems and prospectives of hybrid wheat. In: Genetics and Biotechnology in Crop Improvement. P. K. Gupta, (Ed.), 319-333, 1998.

Tomar, S. M. S. and Anblagan, S.: Characterisation of cytoplasmic male sterile lines in wheat (*Triticum aestivum* L.). *Indian J. Genet.* 64(3), 189-195, 2004.

Virmani, S. S. and Edwards, I. B.: Current status and future prospects for breeding hybrid rice and wheat. *Adv. Agron.,* 36, 145-214, 1983.

Improved Minerals Bioavailability through Phytate Degradation

Asma Maqbool[1], Muzna Zahur[2], Abdul R. Asif[3]

[1]Department of Biological Sciences, Forman Christian College University, Lahore, Pakistan, [2]Department of Biochemistry & Molecular Biology, University of Gujrat, Gujrat, Pakistan, [3]Department of Clinical Chemistry, University Medical Center Goettingen, Goettingen, Germany, E-Mail:asma_cemb@yahoo.com, muzna.zahoor@uog.edu.pk, asif@med.uni-goettingen.de,

Abstract

Phytic acid is a main component of plant seeds and accounts for 1-3 percent of the total weight and 60-90 percent of the phosphorous content in cereals and oil seeds. Together with salt deposition, phytic acid makes a composite compound, phytate, which is considered as an anti-nutrient, due to its chelating activity to the negatively charged divalent minerals, such as calcium (Ca^{2+}), magnesium (Mg^{2+}), zinc (Zn^{2+}) and iron (Fe^{2+}) making them unavailable for absorption. Moreover, phytate also binds to proteins and starch, preventing their assimilation via the digestive system. The presence of phytate in cereals and legumes reduces the bioavailability and uptake of the minerals leading to malnutrition. Owing to the deficiencies of minerals in food, people are facing serious health concerns. Phytase (*myo*-inositol (1,2,3,4,5,6) hexa*kis*phosphate phosphohydrolase) belongs to the phosphatses and has the ability to release at least one phosphate from phytic acid. Phytase supplementation leads to improved bioavailability of minerals and trace elements. In addition to its major application in animal nutrition, phytase is also used for the processing of human food. This is considered as a beneficial approach in foods both from a nutritional and economic point of view. Genetic engineering has become a promising tool for boosting the bioavailability of minerals through hydrolysis of phytic acid by the incorporation of exogenous phytase. Release of transgenic phytase or its enhanced expression in plant biomass, both lead to increased nutrients bioavailability to plants and ultimately to animals and humans. Researchers are looking for novel phytase sources what exhibit potent catalytic features, specific activity and thermal tolerance leading to maximum bioavailability of mineral nutrients in food crops.

Phytic acid/Phytate

The terms phytic acid (PA) and phytate are often used interchangeably even though PA is a free acid and phytate is a salt of PA (Reddy *et al.*, 1989). PA, also known as *myo*-inositol hexa*kis*phosphate, Ins(1,2,3,4,5,6)P$_6$, or InsP$_6$ is the primary phosphorus storage compound in seeds and approximately 70 percent of the phosphate reserves are sequestered into PA (Vats and Banerjee, 2004). The plant seed accumulates PA in protein storage bodies as mixed salts called phytate that chelates a number of mineral cations (Lott, 1984). The phosphate groups confer a high negative charge to this molecule and therefore, a strong chelating ability that reduces the dietary bioavailability of amino acids and minerals, such as Ca^{2+}, Zn^{2+}, Mg^{2+}, Fe^{2+} and potassium (K^+). In small grain cereals, approximately 90 percent of the seed phytic acid is in the aleurone, and the remaining 10 percent in the scutellum. In contrast, in maize 90 percent is found in the scutellum and 10 percent in the aleurone. Almost all PA is present as phytin, a mixed salt (usually with K^+, Ca^{2+}, Mg^{2+} or Zn^{2+}) that is deposited as globoid crystals in single-membrane vesicles together with protein. PA deposition is restricted to cells which remain alive through the quiescent phase of seed development, but it is also found in vegetative tissues and in pollen (Loewus and Murthy, 2000). It is synthesized from *myo*-inositol via a series of phosphorylation steps. PA and its co-precipitated cations are stored in electron dense spherical particles named as globoids (Pfeffer, 1872). The globoids are predominantly localized in the aleurone layer (wheat and barley) or in the embryo (maize) (Odell *et al.*, 1972). The size of the phytate globoids depends on the amount of phytate in the grain. In wild type (WT) wheat, globoid diameters reach up to 4 μm (Antoine *et al.*, 2004), whereas a low PA wheat mutants with the same amount of phosphorus (P) in the grains show lowered phytate concentrations and have smaller globoids (Joyce *et al.*, 2005).

Phytate serves as a major store of phosphorus and *myo*-inositol for growing seedlings (Cosgrove, 1980). During germination, stored phosphorus is necessary for the synthesis of compounds, such as nucleic acids and phospholipids. The free *myo*-inositol can be used as a source of carbon for the growing plant, or serve as a starting molecule for various metabolic pathways. Phytates account for a large component of the organic phosphorus and comprise 20 to 80 percent of the soil organic phosphorus (Dalal 1977; Iyamuremye and Dick, 1996). It is a major macronutrient and acts as a limiting factor in plant growth and development (Wang *et al.*, 2009). Phosphorus based fertilizers are used to avoid phosphorus deficiency and to enhance yield (Richardson *et al.*, 2001). The readily available reserves for phosphorus fertilizer production worldwide may be consumed within 50 to 150 years (Herring *et al.*, 1993). Thus the availability and use of phosphorus as a fertilizer may soon prove to be limiting to world food production (Raboy, 2009).

Phytate and malnutrition

Cereal grains and legumes are taken as a staple diet food in developing countries and reduced bioavailability due to phytates result in an inadequate supply of minerals in this population. Poor bioavailability of these minerals is due to the mineral - phytate complexes, as these complexes cannot be absorbed by the human gastrointestinal tract (Greiner and Carlsson, 2006). Minerals are essential for the activation of intracellular and extracellular enzymes to maintain the pH of body fluids. These enzymes are then involved in the regulation of different metabolic processes and osmotic balance between the cells and their environment. The deficiencies of these minerals can lead to serious complications, which can cause a threat to public health. PA´s antinutrient affects are because of chelating activity with negatively charged divalent minerals (such as Ca^{2+}, Mg^{2+}, Zn^{2+} and Fe^{2+}) and making them unavailable for absorption. Iron and Zn^{2+} uptake is inhibited when the PA:metal ratio increases above 10:1 (Gharib *et al.*, 2006). In human studies, PA presence inhibits absorption of Fe^{2+}, Zn^{2+}, Ca^{2+}, Mg^{2+} and Mn^{2+}, but not copper (Cu^{2+}) (Hallberg *et al.*, 1989; Davidsson *et al.*, 1995; Reddy *et al.*, 1996; Egli *et al.*, 2004).

Mineral uptake depends on several dietary factors, such as the total concentration of an individual mineral, mineral composition, phytate concentration, as well as the concentration of food constituents which promote or inhibit mineral uptake. A great deal of controversy exists regarding the effect of phytates on the availability of dietary iron. Much of this controversy may be due to the low absorption of iron in general, the presence of different iron-phytates with different solubility and the existence of two types of food iron, heme and nonheme iron. Heme iron is found in meat products where it is complexed with porphyrin and accounts for approximately 10 to 20 percent of dietary iron (Carpenter and Mahoney, 1992). It is well absorbed and its absorption is little affected by dietary factors. The second type of iron is non-heme iron from plants. Unlike heme-iron, non-heme iron uptake depends on the composition of the meal and other factors in the degradation pathway. Several studies in humans indicate that phytate has a potent inhibitory effect on iron absorption, therefore the notion that phytate is the major contributor in the reduction of iron availability in humans is well accepted.

Human studies also indicated that phytate inhibits Ca^{2+} absorption, but the effect of phytate on Ca^{2+} availability seems to be less pronounced compared to that of iron. This may be due to the relatively high Ca^{2+} content of plant-based foods, the capability of the bacterial flora in the colon to dephosphorylate phytate and the fact, that Ca^{2+} could be absorbed in the colon. Relatively few studies have dealt with the effects of phytate on dietary Zn^{2+}, Cu^{2+}, Mn^{2+} and Mg^{2+} utilization. Phytates are shown to decrease their bioavailability *in vivo*, but the influence of phytate on Cu^{2+}, Mn^{2+} and Mg^{2+} availability is less marked than those Zn^{2+} and Fe^{2+} (Torre *et al.*, 1991; Greiner *et al.*, 2006).

Phytic acid- minerals, -protein, -starch, and -lipids complexes

It is evident that the effects of PA are attributed to its ability to form complexes with positively charged food components, such as proteins, carbohydrates, minerals and trace elements. The effect of phytates on mineral bioavailability is determined by several factors e.g. pH level, size and valence of the mineral and phytate concentrations, as well as ratios and food matrix, which include the presence of enhancers and/or inhibitors (Weaver and Kannan, 2001). The strong antinutritive effect of phytates (Pallauf and Rimbach, 1996) is also based on the unusual molecular structure. On complete dissociation, the six phosphate groups of PA carry a total of twelve negative charges. Therefore, PA has a strong binding capacity and it effectively binds different mono-, di-, and trivalent cations and their mixtures forming insoluble complexes. It forms fairly stable chelates with almost all multivalent cations, which are insoluble at pH 6 to 7, although pH, type and concentration of cations have a tremendous influence on their solubility characteristics (Reddy *et al.*, 1989). These insoluble phytate mineral complexes in the intestinal tract prevent mineral absorption and thus reduce the bioavailability of essential minerals (Davies, 1982). Rimbach and Pallauf (1992) indicated that regular PA supplementations had a negative influence on Zn^{2+} absorption and lifeweight gain of growing rats.

Phytic acid binds with proteins and starch preventing their assimilation via digestive system (Noureddini and Dang, 2008). It interacts with proteins over a wide pH range, forming phytate-protein complexes due to electrostatic interactions. At a low pH, PA has a strong negative charge due to total dissociation of the phosphate groups while at pH 6 to 7, a ternary PA-mineral-protein complex is formed which dissociates at high sodium (Na^+) concentrations. Under these conditions a negative influence of PA on the solubility of proteins can be expected due to the ionic binding between the basic phosphate groups of PA and protonated amino acid (lysyl, histidyl and arginyl) residues (Urbano *et al.*, 2000; Fretzdorff *et al.*, 1995). Since the isoelectric point of plant proteins is generally around pH of 4 to 5, PA is likely to tightly bind to plant proteins under acidic conditions. In the intermediate pH range (6 to 8), both PA and plant proteins have a negative charge. However, under these conditions complex formation still occurs, possibly by direct binding of PA to protonated α-NH$_2$ terminal groups and α-NH$_2$ groups of lysine residues, and also a multivalent cation-mediated interaction. By binding to plant proteins, PA decreases its solubility and digestibility, consequently reducing its nutritive value. In addition, PA interacts with enzymes such as trypsin, pepsin, α-amylase and galactosidase, which results in a decrease in the activity of these important digestive enzymes (Kerovuo and Tynkkynen, 2000). Besides pH, dietary levels of Ca^{2+} and Mg^{2+}, the source and solubility of protein, also affect protein–phytate interaction (Kemme et al., 1999). Complex formation can adversely affect certain functional properties of proteins, which are dependent on hydration and solubility. In vitro studies have shown that phytate–protein complexes are less likely to be digested by proteolytic enzymes (Ravindran et al., 1995) and even digestive enzymes, such as pepsin, trypsin, chymotrypsin are inhibited by phytate (Kumar et al., 2010). The reduction in the protease enzyme activity might also be partially responsible for poor protein digestibility. Jongbloed et al. (1997) reported that phytate-protein complexes may be formed post feeding in the gut at pH 2 to 3. At this pH level, it was found that soluble proteins in casein, corn, rice polish, soybean meal and sunflower meal were substantially precipitated in the presence of PA. Spinelli et al. (1983) reported that rainbow trout fed purified diets containing 0.5 percent PA suffered a reduction in protein digestibility and about 10 % reduction in growth and feed conversion.

Phytates may also reduce the solubility of starch by binding and hence reducing its absorption and lowering glucose utilization. Phytate-starch binding occurs either directly, via hydrogen bonds, or indirectly via proteins associated with starch (Rickard and Thompson, 1997). In humans, phytate intake reduces the blood glucose response (glycaemic index) (Lee et al., 2006). The effect of PA on starch digestibility correlated with the glycemic index in healthy volunteers. Glycemic index was found to be correlated negatively with the phytic acid content of the food tested (Thompson et al., 1987).

Phytate is a powerful chelator which makes complexes with lipids and other nutrients thereby reducing their digestibility (Vohra and Satyanarayana, 2003). Lipid and calcium phytates may be involved in the formation of metallic soaps in the gut lumen of poultry, which is a major restraint for energy utilization derived from lipid sources (Leeson, 1993). However, there is a paucity of evidence to support the existence of phytate-lipid complexes in humans.

Phytases

Phytase (myo-inositol (1,2,3,4,5,6) hexakisphosphate phosphohydrolase) belonging to class phosphatses with an ability to release at least one phosphate from PA thereby lowering the inositol phosphates. Phytase activity was first reported in the blood of calves (McCollum and Hart, 1908) and rice bran (Suzuki et al., 1907). These early reports on phytase activity indicate the presence of phytases in diverse organisms including bacteria, fungi and yeast. Most monogastrics including humans, lack this enzyme making phytic acid hydrolysis in the gut dependent on mucosal and bacterial enzymes. Details regarding phytase activities have been increased over the years and can be found in other reviews (Vats and Banerjee, 2004; Frontela et al., 2008; Kumar et al., 2011; Escobin-Mopera et al., 2012).

Improvement strategies

Reducing the phytate level effectively by enzymatic and nonenzymatic ways remained a challenge. Enzymatic degradation involves the addition of wild type or recombinant exogenous phytase from various sources, such as fungi (*Aspergillus fumigates*) and bacteria (*E.coli*). Whereas, nonenzymetic hydrolysis can reduce the phytate content during food processing, or the physical separation of phytate rich parts of plants seed. Nevertheless, the consumption of phytases in animal food and their use during food processing are hindered by their thermal intolerance and specific activity. Genetic engineering of phytases is practiced to reduce the phytate content in plants and soil. A brief account of current strategies used to reduce the phytate level is given bellow.

Food Processing

Adverse effects of some phytates on nutrient bioavailability can be reduced by modifying the household food processing and preparation practices such as soaking, germination, malting, cooking, hydrothermal processing and fermentation. These processes result in the hydrolysis of phytates, by increasing the activity of naturally present phytases in plants and microorganisms. Soaking of legume grains and cereal seeds serves as a pretreatment to facilitate processing, which lasts for 15 to 20 min, or even longer, depending on further processing steps. This results in a significant reduction of phytate content because phytate is water soluble and can be removed by decanting the cooking water. The extent of the removal depends on the species, pH, length and conditions of soaking (Perlas and Gibson, 2002).

Malting or germination of cereals and legumes leads to phytate degradation by intrinsic phytase. Plant seeds utilize phytate as a source of inorganic phosphate during germination and thus tend to increase palatability and nutritional value. During germination of cereals and legume, an increase in intrinsic phytate- degrading activity is observed, with a concomitant decline in phytate content (Greiner *et al.,* 2001). The rate of phytate hydrolysis varies with the species and variety, as well as the stage of germination, pH, moisture content, temperature (optimal range 45° to 57°C), solubility of phytates and the presence of certain inhibitors (Egli *et al.* 2004). Moreover, when the malted cereals were ground and soaked under optimal conditions, a complete degradation of phytates was observed (Larsson and Sandberg, 1992). Cooking is not an efficient way for phytate destruction due to its heat stability. Considerable phytate dephosphorylation during cooking only takes place either by discarding the cooking water, or by enzymatic phytate hydrolysis, due to the action of the intrinsic plant phytases during the early part of the cooking phase (Greiner and Konietzny, 1998). Providing plants with exogenous heat-stable phytases is seen as a possibility to improve phytate dephosphorylation during cooking.

Food fermentation is a microbial and enzymatic method for food processing to achieve prolonged shelf life. All commercial phytase preparations contain microbial enzymes produced by fermentation. Microorganisms used for fermentation, may be a part of the natural micro flora found in the raw material that is fermented, or in specially cultivated cultures designed to bring specific changes in the material that is being fermented. The type of microorganism, the fermentation conditions used, and the starting amount of phytate present in the raw material significantly affect the extent of phytate removal during the fermentation process. Phytate reduction occurs throughout the different stages of bread making and obviously depends on the type of bread being made. In oriental food fermentation, however, convincing evidence exists that phytases of the microorganisms used for fermentation contribute significantly to phytate degradation (Fujita et al., 2003).

Transgenic approaches

Many researchers proposed to engineer plants in such a way that they might able to secrete phytases from their roots without phenotypic variations. Reports shows that the phytase extruded into the rhizosphere by overexpressing the exogenous phytase genes having secretary signal peptide can markedly improve the plant phosphorus utilization capability, because of the phytate degradation resulting from the action of phytase. Richardson et al. (2001) were first to generate the transgenic Arabidopsis plants by introducing phytase gene from Aspergillus niger. Various phytase genes have been introduced in plant roots through genetic engineering so far. In transgenic plants phytase are secreted in ample quantities to release phosphate from phytate and exhibit a substantial improvement in utilization of organic phosphorus when kept on phytates as a sole source of phosphorus (Zimmermann et al., 2003; Xiao et al., 2005; Guo et al., 2009). Overexpression of extruded phytase in the rhizosphere could improve the phosphorus utilization, where this enzyme could catalyze the degradation of the phytate and increase the availability of Pi for plants. This transgenic approach requires availability of organic P in the form of phytates in its environment. Transgenic plants accumulated 52% more P than control, when soils were amended with either phytate or phosphate (George et al., 2005a and b).

In order to increase phytate-degrading activity during food processing, incorporation of plants with a high phytase activity into the plant-derived raw material to be processed, is seen as an alternative to the addition of exogenous phytases. The plant's production of phytases can be used to reduce the amount of PA in feed for animals but problems exist regard the stability of the enzymes. High temperature stability is found to be a more reliable approach in generating low PA feed (Brinch-Pedersen et al., 2006). Regarding feed production, the relatively high heat resistance of the A. fumigatus enzyme is an important asset because the enzyme will then be able to withstand the elevated temperatures employed during feed pelleting processes (Wang et al., 2007). Hong et al., (2008) have demonstrated in their studies unique features of genetically engineered sweet potato, where the expression of secretory phytase in transgenic potato improved phytate utilization and increased size, number and yield of potato tubers, when organic fertilizers containing phytate as a sole phytate source were used. Thus, this high-level expression of phytase with high activity over broad pH ranges makes potato tubers a suitable phytase carrier.

Concluding remarks: Scientists ponder about the negative effects of phytate in terms of nutrition. Owing to the deficiencies of minerals in food, people are facing serious health concerns, especially the baby boomer generation. The presence of phytate in an unhydrolysed form reduces the bioavailability and uptake of the minerals leading to the malnutrition. Genetic engineering has become a promising tool for boosting the bioavailability of minerals through hydrolysis of PA by incorporation of exogenous phytase. Nutritionally and economically phytases are considered a gifted approach in food applications. Researchers are more rigorously looking for the best and novel phytate hydrolysing enzymes and ways for optimizing their catalytic features, specific activity and thermal tolerance via genetic engineering for food applications.

References:

Antoine, C., Lullien-Pellerin, V., Abecassis, J. and Rouau, X.: Effect of wheat bran ball-milling on fragmentation and marker extractability of the aleurone layer. J Cereal Sci. 2004;40(3):275-282, 2004.

Brinch-Pedersen, H., Hatzack, F., Stöger, E., Arcalis, E., Pontopidan, K. and Holm, P. B.: Heat-stable phytases in transgenic wheat (Triticum aestivum L.): deposition pattern, thermostability, and phytate hydrolysis. J Agric Food Chem. 2006;54(13):4624-32, 2006.

Carpenter C.E. and Mahoney A.W.: Contributions of heme and nonheme iron to human nutrition. Crit Rev Food Sci Nutr., 31(4): 333-67, 1992.

Cosgrove, D. J.: Inositol phosphates-their chemistry, biochemistry and physiology. Amsterdam: Elsevier Scientific. 1980.

Dalal, R. C.: Soil organic phosphorus. Advances in Agronomy, 29: 83–117, 1977.

Davidsson, L., Almgren, A., Juillerat, M. A. and Hurrell, R. F.: Manganese absorption in humans: the effect of phytic acid and ascorbic acid in soy formula. Am J Clin Nutr. Nov, 62(5): 984-7, 1995.

Davies, N. T.: Effects of phytic acid on mineral availability. In Dietary Fiber in Health and Disease. Vahoung GV, Kritchevsky D. Eds., Plenum Press, New York, 1982.

Egli, I., Davidsson, L., Zeder, C., Walczyk, T. and Hurrell, R.: Dephytinization of a complementary food based on wheat and soy increases zinc, but not copper, apparent absorption in adults, J. Nutr. May, 134(5): 1077-80, 2004.

Escobin-Mopera, L., Ohtani, M., Sekiguchi, S., Sone,T., Abe, A., Tanaka, M., Meevootisom, V. and Asano, K.: Purification and characterization of phytase from Klebsiella pneumoniae 9-3B. J Biosci Bioeng, (In press), 2012.

Fretzdorff, B., Brummer, J. M., Rochen, W., Greiner, R., Konietzny, U. and Jany, K. D.: Reduktion des Phytinsäuregehaltes bei der Herstellung von Backwaren und Getreidenahrmitteln. AID-Verbraucherdienst, 40: 12-20, 1995.

Frontela, C., Ros, G. and Martínez, C.: Application of phytases as functional ingredient in foods. Arch Latinoam Nutr. 2008;58(3):215-20, 2008.

Fujita, J., Shigeta, S., Yamane, Y., Fukuda, H., Kizaki, Y., Wakabayashi, S. and Ono, K.: Production of two types of phytase from Aspergillus oryzae during industrial koji making. J Biosci Bioeng., 95(5): 460-5, 2003.

George, T. S., Richardson, A. E., Smith, J. B., Hadobas, P. A. and Simpson, R. J.: Limitations to the potential of transgenic Trifolium subterraneum L. plants that exude phytase when grown in soils with a range of organic P content. Plant and Soil, 258: 263–274, 2005.

George, T. S., Simpson, R. J., Hadobas, P. A. and Richardson, A. E.: Expression of a fungal phytase gene in Nicotiana tabacum improves phosphorus nutrition of plants grown in amended soils. Plant Biotechnol J. 3(1): 129-40, 2005.

Gharib, A. G., Mohseni, S. G., Mohajer, M. and Gharib, M.: Bioavailability of essential trace elements in the presence of phytate, fiber and calcium. Journal of Radioanalytical and Nuclear Chemistry, 270(1):209-215, 2006.

Greiner, R. and Alminger, M. L.: Stereospecificity of myo-inositol hexakisphosphate dephosphorylation by phytate-degrading enzymes of cereals. Journal of Food Biochemistry.25(3): 229-248, 2001.

Greiner, R. and Carlsson, N.G.: Myo-Inositol phosphate isomers generated by the action of a phytate-degrading enzyme from *Klebsiella terrigena* on phytate. Can J Microbiol. Aug, 52(8): 759-68, 2006.

Greiner, R., Konietzny, U. and Jany, K.-D.: Phytate - an undesirable constituent of plant-based foods? Journal für Ernährungsmedizin 8 (3), 18-28, 2006.

Greiner, R. and Konietzny, U.: Endogenous phytate-degrading enzymes are responsible for phytate reduction while preparing beans (*Phaseolus vulgaris*), J. Food Process. Preserv. 29:321–331, 1998.

Guo, L., Zhao, Y., Zhang, S., Zhang, H. and Xiao, K.: Improvement of organic phosphate acquisition in transgenic tobacco plants by overexpression of a soybean phytase gene Sphy1. Front. Agric. China 3(3): 259–265, 2009.

Hallberg, L., Brune, M. and Rossander, L.: Iron absorption in man: ascorbic acid and dose-dependent inhibition by phytate. Am J Clin Nutr. 49(1):140-4, 1989.

Herring, J. R. and Fantel, R. J.: Phosphate rock demand into the next century: impact on world food supply. Nat. Resources Res. 2: 226-241, 1993.

Hong, Y. F., Liu, C. Y., Cheng, K. J., Hour, A. L., Chan, M.T., Tseng, T.H., Chen, K. Y., Shaw, J.F. and Yu, S.M.: The sweet potato sporamin promoter confers high-level phytase expression and improves organic phosphorus acquisition and tuber yield of transgenic potato. Plant Mol Biol. Jul 67(4): 347-61, 2008.

Iyamuremye, F. and Dick, R. P.: Organic amendments and phosphorus sorption by soils. Adv Agron. 56:139–185, 1996.

Jongbloed, A. W., de Jonge, L., Kemme, P. A., Mroz, Z. and Kies, A.K.: Proc. Sixth BASF Forum on Animal Nutrition, Ludwigshafen, Germany, 1997.

Joyce, C., Deneau, A., Peterson, K., Ockenden, I., Raboy, V. and Lott, J. N. A.: The concentrations and distributions of phytic acid phosphorus and other mineral nutrients in wild-type and low phytic acid Js-12-LPA wheat (*Triticum aestivum*) grain parts. Canadian Journal of Botany-Revue Canadienne de Botanique 83(12):1599-1607, 2005.

Kemme, P. A., Jongbloed, A. W., Mroz, Z., Kogut, J, and Beynen, A. C.: Digestibility of nutrients in growing-finishing pigs is affected by Aspergillus niger phytase, phytate, and lactic acid levels. 2. Apparent total tract digestibility of phosphorus, calcium and magnesium and ileal degradation of phytic acid. Livest. Prod. Sci. 58, 119–127, 1999.

Kerovuo, J. and Tynkkynen, S.: Expression of *Bacillus subtilis* phytase in *Lactobacillus plantarum* 755. Lett Appl Microbiol. 30(4):325-9, 2000.

Kumar, V., Sinha, A. K., Makkar, H. P., De Boeck, G. and Becker, K.: Phytate and phytase in fish nutrition. J Anim Physiol Anim Nutr (Berl). doi: 10.1111/j.1439-0396.2011.01169.x, 2011.

Kumar, V., Sinha, A. K., Makkar, H. P. S., Becker, K.: Dietary roles of phytate and phytase in human nutrition: A review, Food Chemistry. 120, 4: 945–959, 2010.

Larsson, M. and Sandberg, A. S.: Phytate reduction in oats during malting. J Food Sci. 57, 994–997, 1992.

Lee, S. H., Park, H. J., Chun, H. K., Cho, S. Y., Cho, S. M. and Lillehoj, H. S.: Dietary phytic acid lowers the blood glucose level in diabetic KK mice. Nutrition Research, 26(9):474-479, 2006.

Leeson, S.: Recent advances in fat utilisation by poultry, in: Recent Advances in Animal Nutrition in Australia. Armidale, NSW: The University of New England, 170–1981, 1993.

Loewus, F. A. and Murthy, P. P. N.: Myo-inositol metabolism in plants. Plant Science, 150(1):1-19, 2000.

Lott, J.N.A.: Accumulation of seed reserves of phosphorus and other minerals, in: Murray, D.R., Editor, Seed Physiology, Academic Press, New York, 139–166, 1984.

McCollum, E.V. and Hart, E. B.: On the occurrence of a phytin-splitting enzyme in animal tissues. J Biol. Chem. , 4(6): 497-500, 1908.

Noureddini, H. and Dang, J.: Degradation of phytates in distillers' grains and corn gluten feed by *Aspergillus niger* phytase. Appl Biochem Biotechnol. 159(1): 11-23, 2009.

Odell, B. L. and Deboland, A. R.: Koirtyohann SR. Distribution of phytate and nutritionally important elements among morphological components of cereal grains. J. Agric.Food Chem. 20(3): 718-721, 1972.

Pallauf, J. and Rimbach, G.: Nutritional significance of phytic acid and phytase. Arch Tierernahr. 50(4): 301-319, 1997.

Perlas, L. and Gibson, R. S.: Use of soaking to enhance the bioavailability of iron and zinc from rice-based complementary foods used in the Philippines. J Sci Food Agric. 82: 1115–1124, 2002.

Pfeffer, W.: Investigation of the Protein Bodies and the Importance of Aspargins in Seed Germs, in: Pringsheim, N. (Ed.), Annual Science Book of Botany. Verlag von Wilh. Engelmann, Leipzig, 429-574, 1872.

Raboy, V.: Induced mutation-facilitated genetic studies of seed phosphorus Induced Plant Mutations in the Genomics Era. Food and Agriculture Organization of the United Nations, Rome, 173-178, 2009.

Ravindran, V., Bryden, W. L. and Kornegay, E. T.: Phytates: occurrence, bioavailability, and implications in poultry nutrition. Poultry Avian Biol Rev. 6, 125–143, 1995.

Reddy, M. B., Hurrell, R. F., Juillerat, M. A. and Cook, J. D.: The influence of different protein sources on phytate inhibition of nonheme-iron absorption in humans. Am J Clin Nutr. 63(2): 203-7, 1996.

Reddy, N. R., Pierson, M. D., Sathe, S. K. and Salunkhe, D. K., 1989, Phytates in cereals and legumes. CRC Press, Inc. 1989; 345-349.

Reddy, M. B., Hurrell, R. F., Juillerat, M. A. and Cook, J. D.: The influence of different protein sources on phytate inhibition of nonheme-iron absorption in humans. Am J Clin Nutr. 63(2): 203-207, 1996.

Richardson, A. E., Hadobas, P. A. and Hayes, J. E.: Extracellular secretion of *Aspergillus* phytase from *Arabidopsis* roots enables plants to obtain phosphorus from phytate. Plant J. 25(6): 641-9, 2001.

Rickard, S. E. and Thompson, L. U.: Interactions and biological effects of phytic acid. In F. Shaidi (Ed.), Antinutrients and phytochemicals in food Washington, DC: American Chemical Society, 294–312, 1997.

Rimbach, G. and Pallauf, J.: The effect of a supplement of microbial phytase on zinc availability. Z Ernaehrungswiss. 31(4):269-77, 1992.

Spinelli, J., Houle, C. R. and Wekell, J. C.: The effects of phytates on the growth of rainbow trout (*Salmo gairdneri*) fed purified diets containing varying quantities of calcium and magnesium. Aquacult. 1983;30:71-83, 1983.

Suzuki, U., Yoshimura, K. and Takaishi, M.: About the enzyme "phytase", which splits "anhydro-oxy-methylene diphosphoric acid". Bulletin of the College of Agriculture, Tokyo Imperial University, 7: 503-512, 1907.

Thompson, L.U., Button, C. L. and Jenkins, D.J.: Phytic acid and calcium affect the in vitro rate of navy bean starch digestion and blood glucose response in humans. Am J Clin Nutr. 46(3): 467-73, 1987.

Torre, M., Rodriguez, A. R. and Saura-Calixto, F.: Effects of dietary fiber and phytic acid on mineral availability. Crit Rev Food Sci Nutr. 30(1): 1-22, 1991.

Urbano, G, López-Jurado, M., Aranda, P., Vidal-Valverde, C., Tenorio, E and Porres, J.: The role of phytic acid in legumes: antinutrient or beneficial function? J Physiol Biochem. 56(3): 283-294, 2000.

Vats, P., Sahoo, D. K. and Banerjee, U. C.: Production of phytase (myo-inositolhexakisphosphate phosphohydrolase) by *Aspergillus niger* van Teighem in laboratory-scale fermenter. Biotechnol Prog. May-Jun; 20(3): 737-43, 2004.

Vohra, A. and Satyanarayana, T.: Phytases: microbial sources, production, purification, and potential biotechnological applications. Crit Rev Biotechnol. 23(1): 29-60, 2003.

Wang, X., Wang, Y., Tian, J., Lim, B. L., Yan, X. and Liao, H.: Overexpressing AtPAP15 enhances phosphorus efficiency in soybean. Plant Physiol. 151(1):233-40, 2009.

Wang, Y., Gao, X., Su, Q., Wu, W. and An, L.: Expression of a heat stable phytase from Aspergillus fumigatus in tobacco (*Nicotiana tabacum L.* cv. NC89). Indian J Biochem Biophys. 44(1): 26-30, 2007.

Weaver, C. M. and Kannan, S.: Food Phytates, CRC Press. ISBN: 978-1-56676-867-2 eBook ISBN: 978-1-4200-1441-9, DOI: 2001, 10.1201/9781420014419.ch13, 2001.

Xiao, K., Harrison, M. J. and Wang, Z. Y.: Transgenic expression of a novel M. truncatula phytase gene results in improved acquisition of organic phosphorus by *Arabidopsis*. Planta. 222(1):27-36, 2005.

Zimmermann, P., Zardi, G., Lehmann, M., Zeder, C., Amrhein, N., Frossard, E. and Bucher, M.: Engineering the root-soil interface via targeted expression of a synthetic phytase gene in trichoblasts. Plant Biotechnol J. 1(5): 353-60, 2003.

Food Quality Control in Germany

Hans Meliczek

International Society for Sustainable Development and Agriculture, Göttingen, Germany
E-Mail: hmelicz@gwdg.de

Abstract

The assessment of the quality of food is subject to a large number of institutions, rules and regulations depending on numerous criteria, such as whether the produce is sold fresh or processed, whether it is imported or locally produced and what kinds of supplements and additives it contains.

The responsibilities for food quality control are vested with the Federal Ministry of Food, Agriculture and Consumer Protection. It is the task of the Ministry to ensure that all food that is sold in Germany is safe and not damaging to health. The legal basis for official food control is the Food-, Consumer Goods- and Feeding-Code. The supervision over the application of the rules of the food laws is the responsibility of the Ministries of Agriculture of Federal States (Länder). They in turn may delegate control activities to various provincial authorities. This rather detailed subdivision of responsibilities among various institutions requires close coordination in order to avoid overlapping. In addition to these official authorities a number of private, non-governmental institutions, such as local Consumer Centres and Foodwatch as well as several periodicals like Test and Oeko Test Magazine play an important role in food quality control.

All food products that are being sold have to meet clearly defined standards. Processed food has to be marked with labels which provide information on specific ingredients including additives and supplements. In view of an increasing number of persons who give preference to food that is produced without the use of chemical fertilizers and pesticides the significance of different bio-labels is discussed. The paper elaborates on the usefulness and shortcomings of the Minimum Durability Date for specific food items and reviews to what extent this provision leads to the destruction of large amounts of food produced.

Introduction

The assessment of the quality of food is subject to a large number of institutions, rules and regulations depending on a wide variety of criteria, such as whether the produce is sold fresh or processed, whether it is imported or locally produced and what kinds of supplements and additives it contains. There are numerous control criteria depending on the object under investigation.

In Germany food quality control operates within an international context. Comprehensive and internationally recognized standards relating to food, food production and food safety have been developed and are maintained by the Codex Alimentarius Commission (CAC), a body established in 1963 by FAO and WHO. The Codex covers all foods, whether processed, semi-processed or raw with particular focus on foods that are directly marketed to consumers. In addition to detailed standards for specific foods such as the maximum content of additives in certain food items or the maximum residue limits of pesticides and veterinary drugs in specific tissues of certain animals the Codex contains general standards covering matters such as food labelling, food hygiene, food additives and pesticide residues. It also includes guidelines for import and export inspection and for determining the safety of foods derived from biotechnology. All countries of the EU are members of the Codex Alimentarius Commission (FAO/WHO, 2011).

Following the outbreak of several food safety crises in Europe in the 1990s the European Parliament and the Council established in 2002 the European Food Safety Authority (EFSA). It is an authority for risk assessment on food, food safety, animal health and welfare, nutrition and plant protection. ESPA aims at protecting public health and strengthening consumer confidence in the European food supply. Its 460 staff members are assisted by more than 1,500 external scientists. They provide scientific advice on risks in the food chain from farm to fork and communicate on these risks to interested parties and the public at large. EFSA evaluates procedures, substances and claims subject to the regulatory process, such as the scientific substantiation of health claims, nutritional profiles, pesticides, evaluations of maximum residue levels, food additives and GMOs (EFSA, 2009, p. 26). While EFSA is in charge of risk assessment, risk management is the responsibility of the EU-Commission.

Scientists from German research institutions and government representatives are actively involved in the activities of both CAC and EFSA. The results of their work have a binding effect on German food quality control.

Official Food Control Institutions

In Germany responsibilities for food quality control are vested with the Federal Ministry of Food, Agriculture and Consumer Protection. It is the task of the Ministry to ensure that all food that is sold in Germany is safe and not damaging to health. The legal basis for official food control is the Food-, Consumer Goods- and Feeding-Code (BMELV, 2008). Its objective is to protect the consumer against health risks, food deception and defraud. The Ministry issues orders and guidelines for food producers, processors, traders and consumers to guarantee the supply of a balanced, healthy diet and safe foods. These regulations have to be consistent with those of the European Union.

The Ministry is composed of six Departments, two Federal Offices, one for Consumer Protection and Food Security and one for Agriculture and Nutrition, as well as seven Federal Research Institutes, one each responsible for risk evaluation, cultivated plants, animal health, nutrition and food and one for rural areas. The Ministry is housed in two offices, one in Bonn and one in Berlin. It is composed of 83 divisions with a total of over 900 staff members.

The supervision over the application of the food laws is the responsibility of the Ministries of Agriculture of the Federal States (Länder). They have no uniform designation and carry different names such as Ministry of Food and Rural Areas, Ministry of Agriculture, Environment and Consumer Protection, Ministry of Environment, Health and Consumer Protection or Ministry of Transport, Agriculture and Viticulture. These ministries may carry out their own inspections or delegate food control activities to various provincial authorities, such as State Offices (Landesämter) for Consumer Protection and Food Safety.

The actual inspection of food related activities is being conducted by specially trained personnel, in many cases chemists or veterinarians. It takes place at two stages: decentralized inspection of enterprises by district or city authorities and investigations at central laboratories at the level of Länder. Persons who are authorized to conduct food inspections are entitled to enter landed property as well as production and distribution plants dealing with foodstuff and to control relevant documents and records.

This rather detailed subdivision of responsibilities among various institutions requires close coordination in order to avoid overlapping. In the case of diseases or calamities at the national level this may lead to confusion, as was witnessed during the outbreak of the EHEC epidemic in spring 2011. Alleged sources of the origin of the virus were identified differently by different control offices. The ambiguity of identifying the source of the epidemic has caused immense financial losses to innocent agricultural producers. The Federal Audit Office recently reprimanded the crisis management of the government at federal and state levels regarding food control stating that the work of some 400 control offices was not uniformly administered (Zueckert, 2011). In times of increased international commodity trade it is indeed questionable to apply independent control procedures in each of the 16 states.

In 2007 the control authorities of the Länder have scrutinized more than 400,000 food samples in their laboratories. Some 17 percent were related to meat, game and poultry and their by-products, 10 percent to fruits and vegetable and 9 percent to milk and dairy products. Of the total number of samples 15 percent were identified as offences against the law. The authorities also controlled 560,000 enterprises and found fault with 23 percent of them. The main reason for non-compliance was inadequate hygienic conditions (BVL, 2009).

The importance of state control of food quality has become evident in the recent scandals of dioxin content in eggs and in animal fodder, the occurrence of mad cow disease (BSE) and trade with rotten meat ("Gammelfleisch"). Violations of food laws may be punished by monetary fines or imprisonment. In 2005 a merchant in Hamburg who was selling spoiled and mislabelled meat was sentenced to 3 ½ years of imprisonment. In a more recent case the administrative fine for placing rotten meat on the market was Euro 50,000 (BMELV, 2011, p. 8). At the end of November 2011 the owner of a company that was producing and selling Vodka contaminated with Methanol was arrested and his distillery was closed down.

Informal Control Mechanisms

In addition to these official authorities there are a number of private, non-governmental institutions, such as local Consumer Centres and Foodwatch that are engaged in food quality control. There are some 500 Local Consumer Centres in Germany. These associations provide on behalf and with financial support of the government information and legal advice to customers. A particular active agency is the Consumer Centre in Hamburg. It publishes regularly information on instances where producers provide misleading information as to the correct food ingredients. One producer for instance sold instant chicken soup which contained only 1 percent of chicken meat. Other examples are a banana milk drink which contained only 0.1 percent of banana juice concentrate and fried noodles with beef with only 1 percent beef meat (VZ, 2011).

In July 2011 Consumer Centres opened with financial support of the Federal Ministry of Agriculture the internet platform www.lebensmittelklarheit.de. It accepts and publishes consumer complaints regarding packaging and labelling of food. During the last five months the website has received some 300 complaints a week. Since the staff responsible for remedial actions was unable to cope with the task the Federal Ministry of Agriculture has increased its support fund within four months from Euro 200,000 to Euro 975,000. The food industry is rather irritated by this regulation, but several manufacturers have already corrected their labels.

Foodwatch is an NGO that gives advice and information to consumers in all aspects of agricultural and food production. It is a lobby organization of consumers vis-à-vis the food industry. It aims to identify manipulation in food production and checks whether the quality promises made by the manufacturer are in accordance with the actual product.

Foodwatch follows a rather aggressive approach in its mode of operation similar to that of Greenpeace and faces accordingly strong resistance from the food industry.

Food quality control is also taken up by a number of test magazines, the most important being the consumer magazine Oeko Test. It publishes regularly news on the quality of selected food items and other commodities. It does not conduct own research but commissions independent laboratories to do so. On average the magazine tests about 1,000 products monthly. It also considers the Corporate Social Responsibility of the respective enterprise to asses to what extent it adheres to its social responsibility and sustainability. The Foundation Warentest also examines regularly the quality of specific food items, in addition to other consumer goods, and publishes the results in the monthly magazine Test and in the Internet. The foundation appraises the quality of the respective good and bestows ratings from very good to inadequate. Positive ranking marks are being used by the producers as advertisements on the respective packages.

While the above mentioned institutions investigate and report on the quality of food that is already on sale, food producers have the opportunity to avoid negative assessments from the very beginning. They may get the quality of their foodstuff assessed by private research institutes. One of Europe's leading providers of non-medical laboratory analysis is the Institut Fresenius. It provides a complete diagnose service ranging from microbiological examinations, to tests of nutritional value and checks of residues of pesticides and veterinary drugs. The institute issues the Institut Fresenius Quality Seal which guarantees above-average food quality. The German Agricultural Society (DLG) conducts sensory tests of over 27,000 food products and bestows to those that are faultless and meet the quality standards of DLG criteria once a year awards in bronze, silver and gold.

Food and Food Value Labeling

An important means for customers to determine the quality of food is food labelling. The legal bases for food quality control are the Food-, Consumer Goods- and Fodder-Law (BMELV, 2008) and the more detailed Ordinance for Food Labelling (BMELV, 2011).

If labelling of food, particularly of packed food items is done correctly it is an effective means to ensure that the consumer is not deceived or misled about the nature of the food. It provides the consumer with information about the quality of the food so that an appropriate choice can be made. Labels can be used by marketers to attract potential buyers to purchase the product. However, the text has to be big enough so that the consumer has no difficulty to read the text. All obligatory information has to be printed in letters of a size of at least 1.2 mm.

Package graphic design and physical design have become an important and constantly evolving phenomenon.

Nutrition fact labelling is in many cases still optional. The Council of Ministers of the EU has agreed on common regulations for food labelling in June 2011 and it is expected that they will be published in the German Official Gazette in December 2011 and become effective soon afterwards. The majority of German food processors already follow these rules voluntarily.

Food labelling is gaining increased importance, because of a growing trend to processed food, away from fresh food. If food labels are provided, the prescribed content and format must be followed. They should always give information on the energy value, in both kilocalories and kilojoules and the values for a set quantity, usually 100 gr. or 100 ml of the product and also for a defined "serving". This is followed by a breakdown of component elements: fat, protein, carbohydrates, starch, sugar, fat, fibre and sodium. The fat figure may be broken down into saturated and unsaturated fat, while the carbohydrate figure may be subdivided into a subtotal for sugar. Food labels must contain information as to name and address of the producer and the packer. Some food producers declare voluntarily on the packages of their food the content of vitamins, Calcium, Iron and other additives.

In the case of cereals and pulses as well as fruits and vegetables it is obligatory for traders to state the place of origin, in the case of imported goods the country of origin, and the mode of production, i.e. traditional or ecological.

In addition labels may contain free-form marketing information such as: No preservatives, no artificial colour or GMO free. As there is a growing tendency among consumers to buy locally produced food some producers provide on the package the regional origin of the respective food, such as Black forest ham, Luebecker Marzipan or Munich white sausages. In such cases the Federal Patent Court has ruled that the food has to be produced, processed and packaged in the place of origin.

It is forbidden to sell food that has been subjected to ultra-violet or ionised radiation. The addition of antibiotics in food is prohibited.

On the other hand it is allowed for producers to fill synthetic packaging with protection gas, usually Nitrogen, to prevent or reduce the growth of bacteria and mould on cheese, ham and cut bread. The producers of muesli and instant soups may sell fruit and vegetables dried with the help of micro waves.

Food additives that have been assessed and approved for use within the European Union are classified with so-called E-numbers. The numbering scheme follows an International numbering system as determined by the Codex Alimentarius Commission. The system consists of more than 1,500 E-numbers which refer to colouring agents, minerals, preservatives, stabilizers, flavour enhancers, antibiotics and other chemicals. All artificial food colouring and food preservatives as well as taste enhancers and their quantity have to be declared on the labels in terms of E-numbers.

Food ingredients that may cause allergic reactions have to be indicated in a distinct manner, such as in a specific colour. The labels of frozen meat and fish products must show the date of freezing.

In order to protect the consumer against fake food, special orders apply for food imitates, such as analog cheese and glued meat. Their label must indicate the characteristic of the produce and show this on the label in immediate vicinity of the product name.

There is a growing number of persons who give preference to ecologically produced food. In 2001 Germany launched the organic production label "BIO". It is a hexagonal seal surrounding the word BIO and stands for ecological production and welfare-oriented animal husbandry. There are now more than 62,000 products with this label on the market. Over 3,900 companies, particularly those engaged in the trade and processing segments have tapped into this market and use the label (BMELV, 21.9.2011). For new ecologically produced products EU standards prescribe the use of a new BIO label which displays on a green quadrangular background the symbol of a leave depicted by 12 stars.

Rather strict standards of organic food are applied by specialized producer unions, the oldest being Demeter which has been operating according to anthroposophic principles since 1928. The same concept is being applied by Alnatura. Other producers who follow less rigid but still ecological procedures use different brand such as Bioland, Neuland, Naturland and Biopark. They all have to exceed the norms of the ECO regulation EG 834/2007 of the European Union, i.e. have been produced without the use of pesticides and chemical fertilizers, do not contain genetically modified organisms and are not processed using irradiation, industrial solvents or chemical food additives. The control of the origin and quality of organic food is conducted by independent, non-public producer institutions. Each product branded Bio, Eco or Ecological must display the number of the respective Eco control institution.

The Marine Stewardship Council (MSC) Ecolabel certifies sustainable fishing and the application of the best environmental choice in seafood.

There are specific rules for trade with eggs and milk. Trade with eggs has to follow the provisions of the Food Labelling Law (BMELV, 2011) which corresponds to EU-regulations (European Union, 2002). All eggs that are sold must wear an Egg Producer's Code. It is a combination of numbers and letters according to the farming method under which the chicken is raised, the country of origin of the egg, the number of the province and the number of the producer. According to the roaming space available for each chicken EU-Norms classify eggs into: bio eggs (number 0), free range eggs (numbers 1 and 2) and battery caged eggs (Number 3). Battery keeping of chicken is forbidden in Germany since 2007, but is still allowed in other EU countries. These countries may export eggs to Germany, but following a campaign of animal welfare activists (Kein Ei mit der Drei), the sale of eggs with number 3 has decreased in Germany by 60 percent (BUND, 2011). The stamps on the eggs may show the laying date and the date up to which the sale of the egg is recommended.

According to its durability milk is classified into three categories: 1. Fresh milk from the farm with a durability of 2 to 4 days, in sealed containers 6 to 10 days, 2. ESL milk (extended shelf life) up to 3 weeks in sealed containers with a storage temperature of 7 degree Celsius and 3. UHT milk (ultra-high-temperature) in closed containers at room temperature up to 4 months.

Milk with an expired durability date should not be sold. Fresh milk should contain 3.5 to 5 percent fat, while skimmed milk not more than 0.5 percent. Milk containers must provide information about fat content.

The Role of the Consumer

All the above mentioned institutions try to assure the customer that the food bought is healthy and safe. Furthermore the customers themselves have an important influence on the quality of the food they buy and consume. Some 82 percent of customers interviewed in a recent survey consider that the refusal to buy certain commodities is instrumental for improving food quality. They state that it is best not to buy food again with which they have made bad experiences. While some 65 percent believe that it is helpful to lodge a complaint against the trader concerned, only 23 percent of them have made use of this opportunity to press for better food quality by means of criticism. The main reason for this behaviour is a general indolence and the feeling that their engagement would not change anything (SGS Institut Fresenius, 2011).

Many customers have difficulties to recognize the quality of processed food and 50 percent believe that important information on the packing is missing or hidden. Their complaints usually refer to the false information on the ingredients. Some 81 percent recognize a strong relationship between food quality and regular controls (SGS Institut Fresenius, 2011).

Implications of Food Quality Control

According to an order of the Federal Ministry of Agriculture all producers and processors of food have to indicate on their commodity a Minimum Durability Date (Mindesthaltbarkeitsdatum, MHD). This is the date up to which food maintains its original quality. MHD has to specify the expiry date in terms of day, month and year. Up to this date the producers guarantee that the product has under the indicated storage conditions the same nutritional value, colour, nutritional value and taste as it is intended by the producer. The MHD can be fixed by the producer. The MHD has to be applied since 1981 to all food items except fresh fruit, fresh vegetables, wine, salt, sugar and chewing gum (BMELV, 2011, as amended).

The term MHD is a perplexing phenomenon to many customers, since a large number of them assume that the respective food is no longer suitable for consumption after that date. In reality many food items may still be consumed without any risk or negative effect later. In the case of beer for instance the MHD is fixed at 6 to 12 months whereas it is suitable for consumption for several years. Yoghurt has a MHD of 30 days but may be consumed two weeks after this date. Cheese may be eaten without any risk up to 6 weeks whereas its MHD is given with 2 to 4 weeks.

Food that is easily perishable because of its microbiological composition such as minced meat, fresh poultry and fish must be labelled with a consumption date (Verbrauchsdatum). After this date food may not be sold and not be consumed.

In recent months, particularly after the publication of the book "Die Essensvernichter" and after the distribution of the film "Taste the Waste" the general public has become aware of the large amount of food that is wasted and destroyed every day. There are no reliable figures about the amount of food actually destroyed in Germany. The Federal Minister of Agriculture, Ilse Aigner estimates that up to 20 million tons of food are thrown away annually in Germany (Aigner, 2010). Kreutzberger and Thurn (2011) arrive at a similar estimate reckoning that the average German household destroys 100 kg of food per year.

A major reason for this waste is assumed to be the expired MHD as it seems to implicate that the food is no longer suitable for consumption. This assumption is, however only partially true, since other European countries which use a more appropriate connotation for the durability of food, such as: Best before ..., or Da consumarsi preferibilmente entro il... are also confronted with similar food wastage. Langer and Krieg have estimated that on average every European throws away 95 kg of food every year. The food that Europeans throw away would be sufficient to feed all hungry people in the world (Die Welt, 2011).

In addition to the food wasted at the household level some 310,000 tons of food are discarded by shops and supermarkets (i.e. excluding producers and consumers) which amounts to 15 € per capita and year. When the shelves with food items have not been cleared and a new assignment of the same food arrives at the store, the merchants dispose of such food in garbage containers, even if it is sealed in its original package.

It is forbidden by law to grab these items out of garbage containers, even for one's own consumption. Legally such action committed by people, named dumpster divers (Mülltaucher) is considered theft and therefore punishable, but so far police authorities have shown no interest in the pilferage of food they consider "without value" and court cases have been suspended because of "insignificance".

Irrespective of the exact amount of food destroyed there is a growing apprehension against this waste. In order to remedy the situation many cities have created charitable organizations, called "Tafel". These food banks distribute mostly donated food to needy people. Often the product is approaching its "expiration" date or cannot be sold. Volunteers of Tafel groups collect these food items, make sure they are safe to eat and distribute them to people in need. The Tafel organization is supported by more than 50,000 volunteers. It is one of the biggest social movements in Germany. It operates in 800 locations and distributes food to some 1.3 Million persons in about 2,000 distribution centres (BDT, 2011).

How can the waste of food be reduced? The answer is embedded on the consumer's attitude to food and food quality. The problem of food waste can not only be solved by stronger control mechanisms or improved legislation regarding food quality control and food labelling, but requires a change of attitude of the entire population towards the value of food.

References:

Aigner, I.: Die Verbraucher haben Anspruch auf hochwertige und sichere Lebensmittel, Wirtschafts- woche, Düsseldorf, 7.11.2010.

BDT Bundesverband Deutsche Tafel: Essen, wo es hingehört, www.tafel.de, 2011.

BMELV, Bundesministerium für Ernährung, Landwirtschaft und Verbraucherschutz: Pressemitteilun- gen vom 21.9.2011, 179 AI-Biosiegel, 2011.

BMELV, Bundesministerium für Ernährung, Landwirtschaft und Verbraucherschutz: Lebensmittel- kennzeichnungsverordnung, 22.11.1981, zuletzt geändert 29.9.2011.

BMELV, Bundesministerium für Ernährung, Landwirtschaft und Verbraucherschutz: Safety and Transparency Action Plan for Consumer Protection in the Food Chain, 14.01.2011, 12 p. 2011.

BMELV, Bundesministerium für Ernährung, Landwirtschaft und Verbraucherschutz : Lebensmittel-Bedarfsgegenstände- und Futtermittelgesetzbuch (LFGB) , 26.02.2008.

BUND: Achten sie auf den Stempel, www.bund.net/themen_und_projekte /landwirtschaft, 2011.

BVL, Bundesamt für Verbraucherschutz und Lebensmittelsicherheit, Jahresbericht des BVL zur Lebensmittelüberwachung 2008, 2009.

Die Welt, Hamburg, 21.10.2011.

EFSA, European Food Safety Authority: Strategic Plan for 2009 -2013, Parma, 2009.

European Union, Regulation EU-VO 178/2002/EG, Brussels, 2002.

FAO/WHO: FAO/WHO Food Standards, In: www.codexalimentarius.net, 2011.

Kreutzberger, S. und Thurn, V.: Die Essensvernichter, Taste the Waste, Kiepenheuer & Witsch, Köln 320 pp., 2011.

Langer, F. und Krieg, S.: ...und was essen wir morgen? Geo, Hamburg, November 2011, 41, 2011.

SGS Institut Fresenius: Verbraucherstudie, 2011, Lebensmittelqualität und Verbrauchermacht, Taunusstein, August 2011.

VZ, Verbraucherzentrale Hamburg, e.V.: Die Ein-Prozent-Liste, Spurensuche im Kleingedruckten, August 2011.

Zueckert, A.: Rechnungshof rügt EHEC Chaos, Stern, 22.November 2011.

Psychosocial Analysis of the Adoption of Organic Farming in Benin

Ismail Moumouni[1,3], Mohamed N. Baco[1], Florent Gbèdo[1], Silvère Tovignan[1], Guy S. Nouatin[1], Simplice D. Vodouhê[2], Ulf Liebe[3]

[1]Faculty of Agriculture, University of Parakou, Benin; [2]Faculty of Agricultural Sciences, University of Abomey-Calavi, Benin; [3]Faculty of Organic Agriculture, University of Kassel, Germany; Contact: E-Mail: ismailmm@gmail.com

Abstract

Current debate about organic farming emphasizes on the sustainability of farming systems, rural livelihood and food quality and on the technical and economic factors influencing the conversion to organic farming. The paper aims at exploring the psycho-social adoption factors associated with institutional and technical support system set up for the promotion of organic farming, based on a case study in Benin. We carried out this study in Djidja District in South Benin. We conducted semi-structured interviews with two leaders of the Benin Organisation for Promoting Organic Agriculture (OBEPAB) and five agricultural advisers and structured interviews with 100 farmers selected randomly among 255 organic farmers and 50 non-adopters to record why they did not adopt organic farming. We used descriptive statistics correlation for data analysis. We found that important factors which affect the adoption of organic farming were their perceptions of the characteristics of the technology, the economic factors, the institutional support for socio-technical networking and learning and the credit gained by the Nongovernmental Organization promoting organic farming. Farmers' needs for technical competence, social relatedness and farm income safety acted as psychosocial mediators between the technical and institutional support and their motivation to convert to organic farming. Alongside their technical abilities, the capacity of agricultural advisers to cope with psychosocial factors associated with the institutional support systems appears to be crucial in motivating farmers for the adoption of innovation.

Introduction

Current debate about organic farming emphasizes on the sustainability of farming systems, rural livelihood and food quality (Dima and Odero, 1997, Crucefix, 1998, Rigby and Cáceres, 2001, Heaton, 2001, Ferrigno et al., 2005, Hole et al., 2005, Bengtsson et al., 2005) and on the factors influencing the conversion to organic farming (Padel, 2001, Darnhofer et al., 2005). The findings are in line with the three dominant paradigms employed to explain the decision of small farmers to adopt new technology (Negatu and Parikh, 1999). The technology-diffusion models (i) consider the characteristics of technology as determinants of adoption. Sarker and Itohara (2008) identified the simplicity of organic farming technology and availability of basic production factors as the important influential factors related to the organic farming technology. Hong (1994) argues that motivations for organic farming include wanting to follow sound farming practices or reaction against unpleasant experience with agricultural chemicals in Korea. Svensson (1991) pointed out the importance of the profitability in the adoption of organic farming in Sweden. The economic constraints models (ii) emphasize the importance of economic and institutional factors in the adoption of technology. For instance, Bolwig et al. (2009) provided some evidence that product marketing guarantees in relation to receiving a price premium for meeting given quality requirements which reduce smallholders' uncertainty about the net returns to processing of the coffee crop affect the adoption of organic farming in tropical Africa. Kvist (1994) had identified the grant to support organic farming as an important adoption factor in Sweden, especially for farmers still converting new areas. Bruckmeier et al. (1994) supports that, farmers who converted to organic farming followed economic incentives rather than ethically based motivation in East Germany. The technology characteristics-user's context models (iii) argue that farmers' characteristics and subjective perceptions of technology influence adoption. For example, Sarker and Itohara (2008) identified farmers' knowledge and awareness regarding environmental issues, health awareness as influential factors in Bangladesh. Burton et al. (1999) found that organic horticultural producers are more likely to be young, female and small farmers in the UK. Willer and Gillmour (1992) stated that organic producers were motivated primarily by ideological reasons in Ireland. Svensson (1991) in Sweden and Milder et al. (1991) in Saskatchewan found that farmers adopt organic agriculture because they were concerned about environmental degradation and food quality. It comes clearly out that a large range of factors, including significant non-economic variables were identified considered as likely to influence the decision to adopt organic techniques as shown by Conacher and Conacher (1982), Fisher's (1989), Fairweather (1999) and Kallas et al. (2010).

Two important remarks come up from this literature review. First, most of the empirical studies reported have been conducted in the North. Nevertheless, the logic of actions of farmers can vary importantly from community to community, from context to context and even from one farmer to another (Olivier de Sardan, 1995, Cochet, 2006). Some specific characteristics of organic farming in the South are that (i) adopters are smallholders with low formal education and primarily concerned about subsistence, and (ii) farmers must apply for group certification because they cannot afford individual certification; implying mutual control which means that farmers at village levels should control themselves each other. Second, little attention has been devoted to psychosocial analysis, although this can provide us with new insights of the issue (Chouichom and Yamao, 2010, Herzfeld and Jongeneel, 2011). The paper aims at exploring the psychosocial adoption factors associated with institutional and technical support system set up for the promotion of organic farming, based on a case study in Benin. Understanding the nature and mechanisms of those psychosocial phenomena will help for policy making.

Theoretical and methodological framework

We applied the cognitive evaluation theory (Deci and Ryan, 1985, Guay et al., 2001) which posits that individuals progressively develop motivation through their self-evaluations of how competent, socially related and self-determined they are. This theoretical framework is applicable since farming can be considered in many instances as a social activity (Vanclay, 2004). However, we added to this framework the variable of safety of farm income because farming is the main subsistence activity in our study area. We carried out this study in Djidja District in South Benin. Farmers in Djidja are on average 36 years, with generally no formal education. They are heads of households including on average 13 people. The size of the cultivated land is 5.5 ha on average. They undertake agriculture mainly for subsistence. Cotton, maize and groundnut are the main crops. Most households use family labour predominantly. We conducted semi-structured interviews with two leaders of the Benin Organisation for Promoting Organic Agriculture (OBEPAB) and five agricultural advisers to collect data on the institutional and organization support to organic cotton farmers, and on the evolution of the numbers of farmers, seed cotton productions and yields. Structured interviews with 100 farmers selected randomly among 255 organic farmers were conducted. Thereby we (i) measured organic farmers' feeling for competence, social relatedness, self-determination and income security and motivation with Likert Scales, inspired from those developed by Losier et al. (1993), Blais et al. (1993) and Richter and Vallerand 1995 and (ii) collected farmers' opinions about the usefulness of OBEPAB's support and about the requirements of organic farmers (time, input, labour). We interviewed 50 non-adopters to record why they did not adopt organic farming. We used descriptive statistics (means, percentages, graphs) and Pearson correlation for data analysis.

Institutional support to organic farming in Benin

Benin is a West African country with a size of 112,622 sqkm and 2.8 million inhabitants where about 60 percent of people rely on agriculture for subsistence and conventional cotton is the main cash crop that contributes to 13 percent to GDP (MAEP, 2010). The conventional cotton network is facing troubles for bad financial and organizational management. Since the United Nation Conference for Environment and Development in Rio de Janeiro in 1992 has pointed out the necessity to consider the three dimensions of development – environmental, economic and social - in development programmes, many organizations, mostly Non-Governmental Organizations (NGO) have been involved in promoting sustainable and organic farming in Benin. We selected the «Organisation Béninoise pour la Promotion de l'Agriculture Biologique » (OBEPAB) as case study. OBEPAB is a Non-Governmental Organisation established in 1995 which has been the first NGO devoted to organic farming promotion in Benin. The intervention area of OBEPAB includes Djida, Bohicon, Glazoue districts in Southern Benin, and Kandi and Sinende districts in Northern Benin. Organic farming is a form of agricultural production that makes use of natural or organic resources only, as inputs. It is expected to be compatible with environment protection, economically satisfying for the farmer and socially acceptable. OBEPAB focussed its activities on promoting organic cotton as alternative for conventional cotton that makes use of important quantities of synthetic chemical pesticide and fertiliser (Vodouhe, 1997). Bad handling of these products threatens the environment, the sustainability of agriculture and the health of farmers and consumers (Ton et al., 2000, OBEPAB, 2001, OBEPAB, 2002). Alternative technologies, using local natural resources, were developed for cotton pest and soil fertility management.

OBEPAB established a participatory extension system that aimed at developing the analysis competence of the farmer, encouraging his initiatives and valorising his knowledge. Extension workers were committed to close training and supervision of farmers. Farmers are organized at village level in Organic Farmers Associations. Peer visits are organized for farmers to promote experience sharing and networking. OBEPAB played an interface role between farmers and the international market. Each Organic Farmers Associations applied for group certification. A social control system was set up to ensure the respect of the requirement of organic agriculture by the farmer within each association. This social control system is also expected to ease and reinforce solidarity in organic farmers' associations and community. To sum up, the institutional support to organic farmers promoted and ensured:

- Learning (training, farmer field schools, preparation of input, sustainable farming)

- Networking (lively farmer associations, meeting, outside peers visits, mutual control)

- Marketing (group certification, premium of 20 percent on conventional cotton price, guarantee of acceptable income, no payment delay)

To support an effective decision-making, OBEPAB held a database on the evolution of the organic cotton farmers (number of farmers according gender and region), their commitment (cultivated areas), performance (yields, production, etc.) and the premium to organic farmers. As consequence number and production (areas and seed cotton) has impressively increased. From 1996 to 2010, the number of organic farmers has increased from 17 to 2,000 from which 216 are females (Figure 1), the cultivated areas increased from 10 to 425 hectares and the produced seed cotton from 4.8 to 450 tons (figure 2).

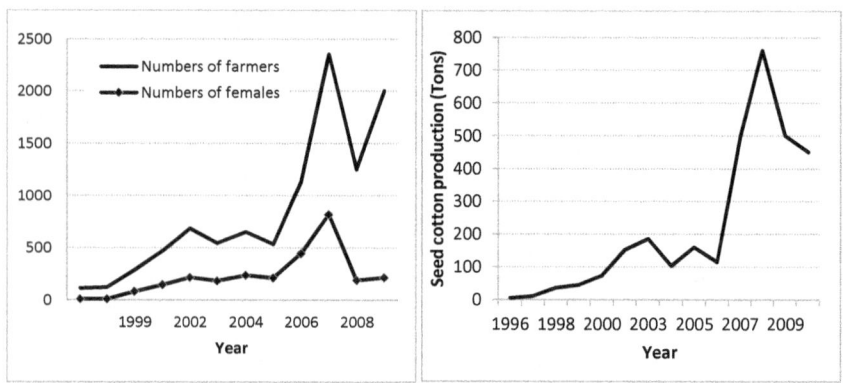

Figure 1: Evolution of the numbers of organic farmers   Figure 2: Evolution of seed cotton production (tons)

What are the main influential factors in converting to organic farming in Benin? Our results show that the lack of transparency in the conventional cotton sector is a favourable situation for the development or organic farming. In addition, the organic farmers' rationales include the need for stable farm income (89.3 percent), acceptable farm income (75 percent) and health issues (35.5 percent). Organic cotton farm income was said to be acceptable because of the premium of 20.9 percent on conventional cotton price for fulfilling the requirement of organic farming. Only 1.5 percent of respondents adopted organic farming for environmental reasons. 91.1 percent of organic farmers appreciated the low requirement of financial capital (fertilizers, pesticides, etc.) in organic farming as they made use of natural resources. A total of 88.4 percent of organic farmers enjoyed socio-technical networking through lively farmer association, peer visits outside the village, collective experiences, solidarity, close and permanent contact with OBEPAB's leaders, etc.). 78.2 percent of them got pleasure in technical learning (frequent trainings and farm visits by the advisers, Farmer Field School sessions, etc.).

Technical constraints for converting to organic farming

The percentages of conventional farmers who perceived organic farming as time and labour demanding, physical constraining and as having low productivity (Figure 3) were higher than those of organic farmers sharing the same opinions (Table 1).

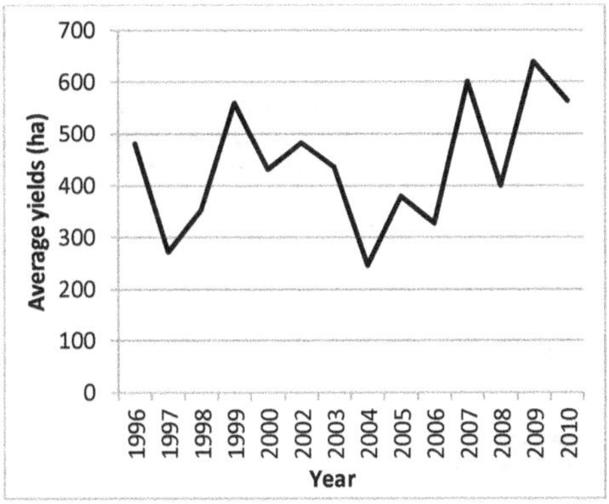

Figure 3: Average yields

Table 1: Perceptions on organic cotton farming

	Percentages of organic farmers (%)	Percentages conventional farmers (%)
Time demanding	30.5	54.5
Physical constraints	10.3	21.8
Labor demanding	08.1	14.6
Low productivity	45.9	65.1

Specially, an important number of organic farmers (30.5 percent) found organic farming to be time demanding and dissatisfied with it low productivity. Farmers must collect natural input (oil palm cake, cowpat, neem leaves, etc.) and prepare their own insecticides and fertilizers. But for most of organic farming adopters, the free access to these input compensated the collection constraints and the premium of 20 percent on conventional cotton price balanced the low productivity. 2.1 percent of farmers showed a compliant behaviour. They could not explain their decision for conversion. This observation made it important to analyse how the institutional support to organic farming influences farmers' cognitive behaviour.

Psycho-social analysis of farmers' motivation to convert to organic farming

The contextual conditions where the adoption of organic farming occurred were characterized by effective (i) socio-technical networking through lively farmer associations, peer visits outside the village, collective experiences, solidarity, close and permanent contact with OBEPAB's leaders, and (ii) technical learning through frequent trainings and farm visits by the agricultural advisers, Farmer Field School sessions, etc. This afforded farmers the possibility to satisfy their sense of social relatedness and competence. The effect of the sense of self-determination on farmers' motivation was low and non-significant (r = 0.23, 0.12). In addition, the social control system (mutual control between farmers for fulfilling organic farming requirement) and close interaction with OBEPAB's field workers which apparently restraint made the farmers feel that their farm income is secured. The motivation to convert occurred when the institutional support system made the farmers feel the satisfaction their needs for social relatedness (r = +0.42 0,00), technical competence (r = +0.64 0,00) and income security (r= +0.53 0,00) (Figure 4).

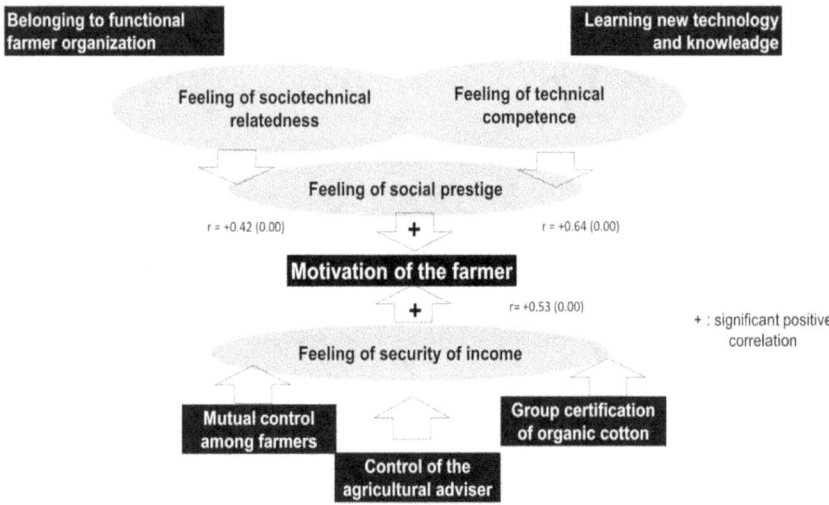

Figure 4: Importance of psycho-social factors in farmers' motivation to convert

Discussion

We found that the main factors which affect the adoption of organic farming were their perceptions of the characteristics of the technology (time demanding, physical constraints, labour demanding), the economic factors (low productivity, low financial requirements, premium, etc.), the institutional support for socio-technical networking and learning and the credit gained by the Non-governmental Organization promoting organic farming. These findings support Conacher and Conacher (1982), Fisher's (1989), Fairweather (1999) and Kallas et al. (2010) who found that many non-economic factors can influence the conversion of farmers to organic agriculture. In opposite, the common environmentalist discourses and some research findings (Dubgaard and Sorensen, 1988, Willer and Gillmour, 1992, Cranfield et al., 2010), and consistent with Bruckmeier et al. (1994), few farmers adopt organic farming for ecological reasons in Benin. Our study brings new insights on how these factors motivate the farmers to adopt organic farming. Contextual conditions such as socio-technical networking (lively farmer association, peer visits outside the village, collective experiences, solidarity, close and permanent contact with OBEPAB's leaders, etc.), technical learning (frequent trainings and farm visits by the advisers, Farmer Field School sessions, etc.) afford farmers the possibility to satisfy their sense of social relatedness and competence and thus lead to motivation. Non consistent with Deci and Ryan's (1985) cognitive evaluation theory, the need for self-determination did not impact farmers' motivation. On the other hand, the social control system, which apparently restraint farmers' autonomy, made the farmers feel that their farm income is secured. Income security seems to be more important for farmers than autonomy. This is consistent with classical motivation theories (see Maslow, 1943, McClelland, 1961, Alderfer, 1969 and Roussel, 2000) presenting the needs for subsistence and security as basic and priority needs. Our results support recent findings such as Herzfeld and Jongeneel (2011) who argue that psychological and sociological literature adding motivational factors should be given more attention in analysing farmers' behaviours.

Conclusion

This paper has provided an application of the cognitive evaluation theory and its usefulness in analysing organic farming adoption processes. The cognitive evaluation theory enlarged to address safety issues helped to explore the interfaces between the institutional support system and the adoption of organic farming. The needs for competence, social relatedness and farm income safety act as psychosocial mediators between the technical and institutional support and the motivation to covert to organic farming. Alongside their technical abilities, the capacity of agricultural advisers to cope with psycho-social factors associated with the institutional support systems appears to be crucial in motivating farmers for the adoption of innovation.

References

Alderfer, C. P.: An empirical test of a new theory of human needs. Organizational Behavior and Human Performance 4(2)142-175, 1969.

Bengtsson, J., Ahnström, J., and Weibull, A. C.: The effects of organic agriculture on biodiversity and abundance: a meta-analysis. Journal of Applied Ecology 42,261-269, 2005.

Blais, M. R., Lachance, L., Vallerand, R. J., Brière, N. M. and Riddle, A. : Échelle de Motivation au Travail (ÉMT-31). Revue Québecoise de Psychologie 14 (3)185-215, 1993.

Bolwig, S., Gibbon, P. and Jone, S.: The economics of smallholder organic contract Farming in Tropical Africa. World Development 37(6) 1094–1104, 2009.

Bruckmeier, K. H. Grund, D., Symes, and Jansen, A. J.: Perspectives for environmentally sound agriculture in east Germany: Agricultural Restructuring and Rural Change in Europe, Wageningse Sociologische Studies 37, 180–194. Wageningen Agricultural University, The Netherlands, 1994.

Burton, M., Rigby, D. and Young, T.: Analysis of the determinants of adoption of organic horticultural techniques in the UK. Journal of Agricultural Economics 50(1)4, 7-63, 1999.

Chouichom, S. and Yamao, M.: Comparing opinions and attitudes of organic and non-organic farmers towards organic rice farming system in North-Eastern Thailand. Journal of Organic Systems 5(1)25-35, 2010.

Cochet, H. : Etat des savoirs sur les mondes ruraux africains. Etudes africaines /état des lieux et des savoirs en France. 1re Rencontre du Réseau des études africaines en France, 29-30 novembre et 1er décembre 2006, Paris, 2006.

Conacher, A. and Conacher A.: Organic farming in Australia. Geowest No. 18. The Department of Geography, University of Western Australia, Nedlands, 1982.

Crucefix, D.: Organic Agriculture and Sustainable Rural Livelihoods in Developing Countries. Natural Resources and Ethical Trade Programme, UK, 1998.

Darnhofer, I., Schneeberger, W. and Freyer, B.: Converting or not converting to organic farming in Austria: Farmer types and their rationale. Agriculture and Human Values 22, 39-52, 2005.

Deci, E. L. and Ryan, R. M.: Intrinsic motivation and self-determination in human behavior. New York: Plenum , 1985.

Dima, S. J. and Odero, A. N.: Organic Farming for Sustainable Agricultural Production: A Brief Theoretical Review and Preliminary Empirical Evidence. Environmental and Resource Economics 10, 177–188, 1997.

Cranfield, J., Henson, S. and Holliday, J.: The motives, benefits, and problems of conversion to organic production. Agriculture and Human Values 27, 291–306, 2010.

Dubgaard, A. and Sorensen, S. N.: Organic and biodynamic farming in Denmark: a statistical survey. Rapport, Statens-Jordbrugsokonomiske Institut, Denmark, No.43, 1988.

Fairweather, J. R.: Understanding how farmers choose between organic and conventional production: Results from New Zealand and policy implications. Agriculture and Human Values 16, 51–63, 1999.

Ferrigno, S., Ratter, S. G., Ton, P., Vodouhe, D. S., Williamson, S. and Wilson, J.: Organic cotton: a new development path for African smallholders? The Gatekeeper series 120. International Institute for Environment and Development. London, 2005.

Fisher, P.: Barriers to the adoption of organic farming in Canterbury." M. Appl. Sci. Thesis. Centre for Resource Management, Lincoln College, 1989.

Guay, F., Boggiano, A. K. and Vallerand, R. J.: Autonomy support, intrinsic motivation, and perceived competence: conceptual and empirical linkages. Personality and Social Psychology Bulletin 27(6) 643-650, 2001.

Herzfeld, T. and Jongeneel, R.: Why do farmers behave as they do? Understanding compliance with rural, agricultural, and food attribute standards. Land Use Policy 29, 250– 260, 2011.

Heaton, S.: Organic farming, food quality and human health: A review of the evidence. Soil Association, Bristol, 2001.

Hole, D. G., Perkins, A. J., Wilson, J. D., Alexander, I. H., Grice, P. V. and Evans, A. D.: Does organic farming benefit biodiversity? Biological Conservation 122(1)113-130, 2005.

Hong, C. W.: Organic farming and the sustainability of agriculture in Korea," Extension-Bulletin, ASPAC, Food and Fertilizer Technology Center No. 388, 1994.

Kallas, Z., Serra, T. and Gil, J. M.: Farmers' objectives as determinants of organic farming adoption: the case of Catalonian vineyard production. Agricultural Economics 41, 409–423, 2010.

Kvist, M.: Evaluation of the grant to organic production," Jordbruksekonomiska Meddelanden 56(12)1302–1322, 1994.

Losier, G. F., Vallerand, R. J., and Blais, M. R. : Construction et validation de l'Échelle des Perceptions de Compétence dans les Domaines de Vie (EPCDV). Science et comportement 23, 1-16, 1993.

Ministère de l'Agriculture de l'levage et de la Pêche (MAEP) : Plan stratégique de relance du secteur agricole (PSRSA). Version Finale, 2010.

Maslow, A.: A theory of human motivation. The Psychological Review 50(4) 370-396, 1943.

McClelland, D. C.: The Achieving Society. New York: Van Nostrand Reinhold, 1961.

Molder, P. J., Negrave, P. D. and Schoney R. A.: Descriptive analysis of Saskatchewan organic producers. Canadian Journal of Agricultural Economics 394(2)891–899, 1991.

Negatu, W. and Parikh, A.: The impact of perception and other factors on the adoption of agricultural technology in the Moret and Jiru Woreda (district) of Ethiopia. Agricultural Economics 21, 205-216, 1999.

OBEPAB : Rapport sur les accidents causés par les pesticides chimiques de synthèse utilisés dans la production cotonnière au Bénin. Cotonou, 2001.

OBEPAB : Le Coton au Bénin: Rapport de consultation sur le coton conventionnel et le coton biologique au Bénin, Rapport du Projet Pesticides Poverty and Livelihoods, PAN UK, 2002.

Olivier de Sardan, J.-P. : Anthropologie et développement, essai en socio-anthropologie du changement social. Paris: Karthala, 1995.

Padel, S.: Conversion to Organic Farming: A Typical Example of the Diffusion of an Innovation? Sociologia Ruralis 41(1)40-61, 2001.

Richer, S., and Vallerand, R. J. : Construction et validation de l'Échelle du sentiment d'appartenance sociale en milieu de travail. Communication présentée lors du congrès annuel de la SQRP, Ottawa, ON, 27-29 octobre, 1995.

Rigby, D. and Cáceres. D.: Organic farming and the sustainability of agricultural systems. Agricultural Systems 68(1)21-40, 2001.

Roussel, P.: La motivation au travail – Concept et théories. LIRHE Note n°326. Toulouse : LIRHE, 2000.

Sarker, A. and Itohara, Y.: Factors influencing the extent of practice of organic farming technologies: A case stuty of Tangail district in Bangladesh. American Journal of Agricultural and Biological Sciences 3(3)584-590, 2008.

Svensson, I.: "Governmental subsidy to organic farming 1989. A mail inquiry." Alternativ-Odling No. 7, 1991.

Ton, P., Tovignan, S. and Vodouhe, S.: Endosulfan deaths and poisonings in Benin. Pesticide News 47, 2000.

Vanclay, F.: Social principles for agricultural extension to assist in the promotion of natural resource management. Australian Journal of Experimental Agriculture 44(3) 213-222, 2004.

Vodouhe, S. : Le coton biologique, une chance à saisir pour l'Afrique pour un développement plus harmonieux. Abomey-Calavi, 1997.

Willer, H. and Gillmor, D. A.: Organic agriculture in the Republic of Ireland. Irish Geography 25(2)149–159, 1992.

Acknowledgement: We would like to thank the International Foundation for Science (IFS) for financing this study.

Analysis of Vetiver Oil Supply Chain in Indonesia

Heti Mulyati[1], Alim Setiawan S.[2], and Meika S. Rusli[3]

[1] Ph.D student at Chair of Production and Logistics, Faculty of Economic Sciences, University of Göttingen, Germany and Lecturer at Department of Management, Faculty of Economics and Management, Bogor Agricultural University, Indonesia
[2] Lecturer at Department of Management, Faculty of Economics and Management, Bogor Agricultural University, Indonesia
[3] Lecturer at Department of Agroindustrial Technology, Faculty of Agricultural Technology, Bogor Agricultural University, Indonesia

E-mail : [1]heti.mulyati@wiwi.uni-goettingen.de, heti@ipb.ac.id; [2]alimss@ipb.ac.id, [3]mrusli@ipb.ac.id

Abstract

The essential oils of vetiver are one of the agro-industrial commodities that are very well known and have become one of the main commodity exports of Indonesia. The essential oil of vetiver's competitiveness can be achieved through integrated supply chain systems. The research objectives are to analyze the potential of vetiver oils and value added of vetiver oil. Data were collected through observation, in-depth interviews, and focus group discussions. The sampling method was purposive and snowball sampling.

Primary members of the vetiver oil supply chain consist of farmers, vetiver root collectors, distillers, vetiver oil collectors, and exporters. The members of the chain are classified as Small Medium Enterprises (SME's) except exporters. They cluster in Garut Regency West Java and spread over in five Sub-districts namely Bayongbong, Samarang, Cilawu, Leles and Pasir Wangi, while the exporters are located in Bogor, Sukabumi and Jakarta. Partnerships between farmers, distillers, collectors or exporters consist usually of long term relationships based on trust. The big problems faced in the vetiver supply chain are low quality, low yield and the use of simple technology. Value added of vetiver oils is higher in the dry season (IDR 2,537.38/kg) than in the wet season (IDR 887.38/kg). The difference of value added between two seasons is about 65 percent.

Introduction

The essential oil of vetiver or java vetiver oil has been an important export agro-commodity of Indonesia in the past and has great potential for the future. Essential oils of vetiver are widely used as raw materials for perfumes, fragrance, cosmetics, soap, pharmaceuticals, and insect repellents since ancient times (Indrawanto, 2006). Vetiver oil is obtained from vetiver roots (*Vetiveria zizanoides* L.) which are at least 18 months old. The roots of this grass yield an essential oil on steam distillation. Haiti Island in the Caribbean is the major source for the supply of vetiver oil to the world market, followed by Java (Indonesia). Indonesia's export value increase around 38 percent each year (UN Comtrade, 2008). The value of Revealed Competitive Advantage (RCA) is higher than in other countries (6.2) as the value of RCA of France, Switzerland, United States and United Kingdom is 1.08 respectively 4.02; 0.52, and 0.37 (Mulyati *et.al*, 2009).

The leading producers of vetiver oil in Indonesia were located in Garut Regency, West Java, which is spread in five regions namely Samarang, Bayongbong, Cilawu, Leles, and Pasir Wangi. They cluster in an industrial cluster of vetiver oil which is centered in the District Samarang. The vetiver oil is exported to several countries such as Japan, China, Singapore, India, Hong Kong, the United States, Britain, Holland, France, Germany, Belgium, Switzerland and Italy (Ministry of Industry, Republic of Indonesia, 2007). Essential oils of vetiver are produced by small-medium enterprises (SME's) distillers. Most of them use simple and traditional steam distillates. Consequently, they are not able to meet the required quantity and quality of the world market. Furthermore, vetiver oils SME's face many other problems such as lack of information, gap of income along the supply chain members, long supply chain, and lack of financial resources. If these conditions continue, the vetiver oil SMEs will not be sustained.

In view of the existing conditions of the vetiver oil supply chain the objective should be to maximize the overall value generated. A supply chain consists of all parties involved, directly or indirectly, in fulfilling a customer request. The supply chain includes not only the manufacturers and suppliers, but also transporters, warehouses, retailers, and even customers themselves. A typical supply chain may involve a variety of stages. These supply chain stages include raw materials suppliers, manufacturers, wholesalers or distributors, retailers and customers. Each stage in a supply chain is connected through the flow of products, information, and funds. These flows often occur in both directions and may be managed by one of the stages or an intermediary (Chopra and Meindl, 2007). In other words, a supply chain consists of multiple firms, both upstream (i.e. supply) and downstream (i.e. distribution) and the ultimate consumer. A supply chain is defined as a set of three or more entities (organizations or individuals) directly involved in the upstream and downstream flows of products, services, finances, and/or information from a source to a customer (Mentzer et al., 2001).

A supply chain must be managed to achieve competitive advantage. It encompasses all activities associated with the flow and transformation of goods from the raw materials stage (extraction), through to the end user, as well as the associated information flows. Materials and information flow both up and down the supply chain. Supply change management is the integration of these activities through improved supply chain relationship to achieve a sustainable competitve advantage (Balou, 2004).

As a philosophy, SCM takes a systems approach to viewing the supply chain as a single entity rather than a set of fragmented parts, each performing its own function (Ellram and Cooper, 1990; Houlihan, 1988; Tyndall et al., 1998; Mentzer et al., 2001). Chopra and Meindl (2007) stated that successful supply chain management requires many decisions relating to the flow of information, product and funds. Fawcett et al., (2007) stated that the objective of SCM is to design a seamless value added process across organization boundaries to meet the real needs of the end customers. Successful supply chain management requires many decisions relating to the flow of information, product, and funds.

Another important thing in SCM is value-added. Value added is defined as process in which a good or service is stripped down to its essential attributes or benefits. Those that contribute to the customer appeal are enhanced, the others are reduced or eliminated. The value a supply chain generates is the difference between what the final product is worth to the customer and the costs the supply chain incurs in filling the customer's request.

The objectives of this research are to analyze the vetiver oil supply chain and value added of vetiver oil in Indonesia. Finally, we recommend strategies to improve the vetiver oil supply chain performance. Thus, it can be beneficial to many stakeholders related to the vetiver oils supply chain such as government, community and business.

Research method

The study was conducted in the form of a case study. This required the ability to generate answers to questions such as "Who", "What", "Why" and "How" that enable the researcher to gain a rich understanding of enacted within a given context while drawing attention to differences and similarities (Yin, 1994). The research was conducted from February to August 2011. The location of the study was Garut Regency, West Java which is the centre of vetiver oil production in Indonesia, while the exporters were located in Jakarta, Sukabumi and Bogor.

Information was obtained from primary and secondary data. Primary data were collected through observations, focus group discussions, and structured interviews. Secondary data were collected from UN Comtrade, Indonesia Central Bureau of Statistics, Ministry of Industry, Republic of Indonesia (RI), Ministry of Agriculture, RI, and relevant literature.

Sampling was done by snowball and purposive sampling. Sampling of farmers was considerably difficult as it was not easy to identify all the members of the desired population. The sample was selected using snowball sampling. In this particular sampling technique, the researcher initially made contact with a leader of *Usaha Rakyat* (*Usar*) Cooperation and asked some other members belonging to the same population. The researcher made contact with identified members, those members were asked to further name some other members of the population. This process was continued until the desired sample size was reached. The distillers were selected purposively considering location and business sustainability. Respondents consisted of farmers (25 persons), distillers (12 persons), vetiver root collectors (3 persons), vetiver oil collectors (2 persons), and exporters (1 person). The number of respondents and their location is displayed in Table 1.

Table 1. Number of Respondents

No	Sub district	Respondents				
		Farmers	Distillers	Vetiver root collectors	Vetiver oil collectors	Exporter
1	Samarang	10	5	2	-	-
2	Bayongbong	7	4	1	1	-
3	Cilawu	7	2	-	-	-
4	Leles	1	1	-	-	-
5	Garut Kota	-	-	-	1	-
6	Bogor	-	-	-	-	1
	Total	**25**	**12**	**3**	**2**	

Data analysis was done by using descriptive analysis and Hayami method value-added analysis. Value-added is the difference between input costs and output value. The value-added along the supply chain can be tangible goods added and intangible services supplied

(Hines, 2004). Value-added is all the additional value created at a certain stage by production factors, including tangible added value through the transformation of raw materials, labor and capital goods, as well as intangible added value through intellectual capital (use of knowledge assets) and an exchange relationship (i.e. building cooperative relationship). Value added of vetiver oils was obtained by counting one production cycle.

According to Hayami et al. (1987), tangible added value is influenced by technical factors (production capacity, amount of raw materials used and labor) and market factors (output price, wage of labor, raw materials prices, and value of other inputs). It can be formulated as follows in Table 2.

Value-Added = f {K, B, T, U, H, h, L}   (1)

K = production capacity, B = used raw materials, T = labor, U = wage labor, H = output price, h = raw materials price, L = value of other *inputs* (value and all the sacrifices that occurred during the processing to add value)

Table 2. Value added Analysis using Hayami Method

No	Output, Input and Price	Formulas
Output, Input, and Price		
1	Output (kg)	(1)
2	Raw material input (kg/day)	(2)
3	Labour input (Hour/Day)	(3)
4	Conversion factor	(4)= (1)/(2)
5	Labour coefficient (Hour/kg)	(5)= (3)/(4)
6	Product price(IDR/kg)	(6)
7	Wage rate (IDR/Hour)	(7)
Income and Profit		
8	Raw materials Input (IDR/kg)	(8)
9	Other current inputs(IDR/kg)	(9)
10	Product (IDR/kg)	(10) = (4) x (6)
11	a. Value-added (IDR/kg)	(11a) =(10) – (8) – (9)
	b. Value-added ratio (%)	(11b)= (11a)/ (10) x 100
12	a. Labor income (IDR/kg)	(12a) = (5) x (7)
	b. Labor share (%)	(12b) = (13a) / (10) x 100
13	a. Processor profit (IDR/kg)	(13a) = (11a) – (12a)
	b. Profit rate (%)	(13b) = (13a) / (10) x 100
Owner Compensation Factor of Production		
14	Margin (IDR/kg)	(14) = (10) – (8)
	a. Direct labor income (%)	(14a) = (12a) / (14) x 100
	b. Donation of other inputs (%)	(14b) = (9) / (14) x 100
	c. Company profits (%)	(14c) = (13a) / (14) x 100

Source : Hayami et al. (1987)

Results and discussion

Vetiver oil supply chain is similiar to the essential oils supply chain. Primary members of the vetiver oil supply chain consist of farmers, vetiver root collectors, distillers, vetiver oil collectors, and exporters. The members of chain classified as Small Medium Enterprises (SME's) except exporters. Physical flow starts from farmers or farmer groups who delivered their produce to root collectors or to distillers who distillate directly, or ship to vetiver oil collectors and exporters. In contrast, financial and information flow originated from exporters, vetiver oil collectors, distillers, and farmers or farmer groups. The vetiver oils supply chain in Indonesia is shown in Figure 1 .

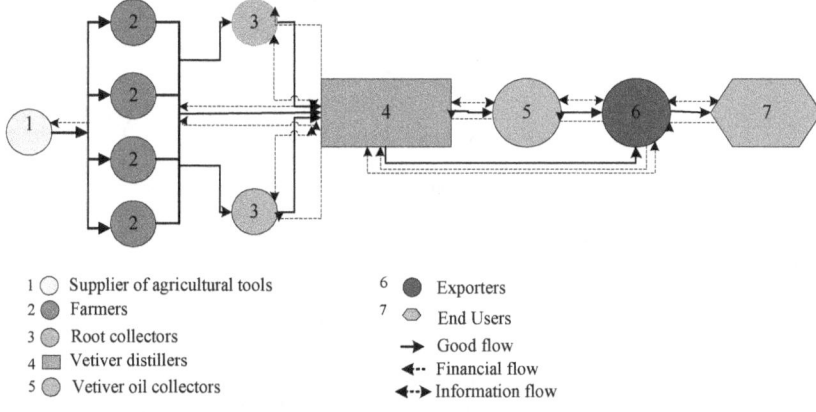

1 ◯ Supplier of agricultural tools
2 ● Farmers
3 ◯ Root collectors
4 ▨ Vetiver distillers
5 ◯ Vetiver oil collectors
6 ● Exporters
7 ◌ End Users
→ Good flow
◀·· Financial flow
◀··▶ Information flow

Figure 1. The Vetiver Oils Supply Chain in Indonesia

Farmers

Farmers lived in five Sub-districts, namely Bayongbong, Samarang, Cilawu, Leles and Pasir Wangi. The study covered 1,203 farmers with a workforce of 52,717 persons. They were classified as individual and group farmers. A total of 33 farmer groups were located in Samarang (9), Leles (12), Cilawu (10) and Bayongbong (2). The land area for vetiver cultivation was 2,400 ha, spread in Samarang (750 ha), Bayongbong (210 ha), Cilawu (240 ha), and Leles (750 ha).

A group farm was chaired by a distiller who acted as financier and trainer for vetiver cultivation for its members. Members of farmer groups provided means of crop production such as fertilizer, seeds, pesticides, and labor. A member must comply with all regulations that have been agreed by both parties and his crops should be purchased by his chairman. However, there are several distillers who gave freedom to its members to sell their produce to other groups or distillers. The farmer groups usually are incorporated in a Usar cooperative.

Land ownership of farmers was distributed as follows: self-owned (88%), rent (4%), self-owned and rent (8%). The cultivation of vetiver consists of monoculture (16%) and mixed crop cultivation (84%) between potatoes and carrots. Vetiver farmers classified as small-scale farmers because most of them cultivate areas smaller than 5 hectares (Figure 2.)

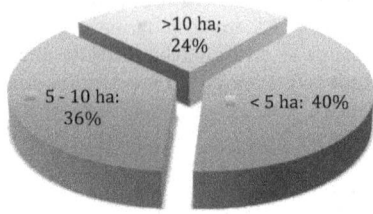

Figure 2. Farmers Cultivating Land Area

The locations of the areas under vetiver land cultivation were disperse and difficult to reach. Because of this situation the root collectors play an important and dominant role in vetiver root trade. The sales of vetiver experience no significant constraints, since all crops were bought by the next chain member (root collectors and distillers). Cooperation between farmers, collectors, and distillers has a positive effect on the vetiver root sales. The price of vetiver root is IDR 1,200-IDR 3,000 per kg but most farmers sell it at IDR 2,000 per kg. The imbalance between selling price and production costs causes some farmers to ignore good agricultural process. They tend to cultivate vegetables such as potatoes or carrots to improve their income because of necessity for their household expenses. This situation causes the lack of vetiver roots as raw material. Farmers who plant vetiver according to good cultivation methods are estimated to amount to only 10%. Moreover, the plants are normally harvested after 7 to 9 months whereas the correct harvest time should be a minimum of 12 months. There is a decreasing trend in the area under vetiver cultivation which has decreased by about 50 percent. In 2006, the potential area of vetiver was 2,500 hectares but the actual area under cultivation is only about 1,200 hectares.

Capital for cultivation originates mostly from themselves, their families, and the leader of their farmer group. Farmers did not get loans from financial institutions because this requires complicated administrative procedures and needs collaterals. The big problem is the length of cultivation (12 months). Because of the debt bondage system or *ijon* most farmers are forced to sell vetivers already after 8 months.

Vetiver root collectors
Vetiver root collectors gather the vetiver root based on debt bondage (ijon system). They determine a certain price for the amount of vetiver root before it is harvested. Root collectors get some money from distillers to find the vetiver root. The average amount which can be collected by root collectors is about 4 – 5 tons per day with a price of IDR 2,000 – 3,000 per kg. The price is paid directly after the delivery of the vetiver roots or on a cash-carry system. Root collectors joint to the partnership and get some information about good cultivation and distillation techniques.

Vetiver distillers

Vetiver distillers play an important role in the vetiver supply chain as they produce crude vetiver oils. They are dispersed in four regions, namely Samarang, Bayongbong, Cilawu and Ieles. The largest distillers are located in Samarang (42 percent). Most of them (75 percent) are members of a *Usar cooperative*. The location *of the Usar cooperative* in Samarang is a central vetiver oil cluster. The cooperative forms a partnership between farmers or farmer groups, distillers, and root collectors. They discuss good agricultural processes of vetiver cultivation, good manufacturing processes of vetiver, and share information on price and quality. The cooperative conducts regular meetings each month. Partnerships between farmers, distillers, collectors or exporters are usually based on a long term relationship. The members usually discuss about the quality of vetiver oils. The other partnership which exists between distillers and fuel suppliers as well as suppliers of machines is a short term relationship.

The distillers obtain the vetiver roots from farmers, root collectors, and themselves. Most of the distillers conduct water steam distillation with non-stainless steel machines/equipments (80 percent) and the others use boilers or steam generators (20 percent) with stainless steel equipment. Non-stainless steel equipments produce low quality oils. In addtion, the temperature and pressure are not set up accordance with the standards (Good Manufacturing Process) and the separation process of water and oil is still conducted traditionally. Many distillers sell their oils to vetiver oil collectors and exporter representatives in Garut (80 percent) and the others sell directly to exporters in Jakarta, Bogor and Sukabumi.

The start up capital for vetiver oils business needs more than IDR 200 millions. Some distillers are unable to meet this requirement. Most of distillers (75 percent) didn't borrow a loan from a financial institution or a bank. Others (17 percent) have been given a grant from the Ministry of Small Medium Enterprises (SMEs), Republic of Indonesia and the remaining 8 percent of the distillers have borrowed a loan from a bank. They got the initial capital from themselves, exporters, oil collectors, or from a combination of distillers, oil collectors, and exporter.

Problems that are faced by distillers are inconsistent raw material availability, low quality of raw material which is not standard-compliant, and expensive fuel price. Furthermore, most of them still use simple or traditional technology which causes low-quality vetiver oils. Most of distillers depend on a loan from collectors or exporters. They repay their loan in the form of vetiver oil.

Vetiver oil collectors

A vetiver oil collector is a representative of an exporter. The study covered two collectors. They pay distillers in accordance with a cash and carry system. The collectors can gather 100 – 400 kg oil in a week during July to September (major harvest season), but from March to June the amount of vetiver oils they can collect is 20 kg per 10 days. Distillers will deliver their oils to collectors without any formal agreement. The collectors will provide information about the prices and quality that is needed in the world market. They also inform about loans needed to run the business. The relationship between distillers and collectors is based on trust and long term relationship. Distillers will trust the collectors about the price and quality of vetiver oils because the collectors have many years experiences in vetiver oils trade. But collectors don't know the exact world market price. They only get this information from exporter.

The problems that are often faced by collectors are irregular availability of vetiver oils and the low quality of oils.

Exporters

Exporters are at the end of the vetiver oil supply chain in Indonesia. Exporters who are located in Jakarta, Bogor, and Medan get vetiver oils from vetiver oil collectors or distillers directly. The price is determined by exporters using the organoleptic test which is based on product quality. But, there is no standard price based on the level or levels of quality or content of essential compounds in vetiver oil products. Exporters have the right to reject vetiver oil that does not fit the standard. In such cases refiners sell oil to other exporters.

The process of mixing low-quality vetiver oil with good quality oil generally occurs at the level of the exporter. Exporters not only export the vetiver oil but also other essential oils such as patchouli oil, clove oil and spices. They export the 2nd and 3rd grade quality to Asia countries, while the 1st grading quality is exported to the US and Europe such as France and Germany. The agreement between distillers and exporters is that the oils should be sold to exporters if the distillers accepted a loan from the exporter. The payment mechanism from the end consumers to the exporter is cash. Exporter pays to distillers or oils collectors in cash after the oils have been delivered.

Value-added analysis

Value-added of vetiver oil are grouped into two categories i.e wet and dry season. Value added of vetiver oils in dry season higher (IDR 2,537,38/kg) than wet season (IDR 887.38/kg). The difference of value added between two seasons is about 65 percent. The value added of vetiver oils is as follows (Table 3).

Table 3. Value- Added of Vetiver Oils

No.	Output, Input and Price	Unit	Value Added	
			Wet Season	Dry Season
1.	Output	Kg/production	5.00	8.00
2.	Raw materials Input	Kg	2,000.00	2,000.00
3.	Labor	Hour/production	12.00	12.00
4.	Conversion factor		0.0025	0.004
5.	Labor coefficient	Hour/kg	0.006	0.006
6.	Product price	IDR/kg	1,100,000.00	1,100,000.00
7.	Wage rate	IDR /hour	12,500.00	12,500.00
8.	Raw material input	IDR /kg	1,333.33	1,333.33
9.	Other current	IDR /kg	529.29	529.29
10.	Output value	IDR /kg	2.750.00	4,400.00
11.	Value-added	IDR /kg	887.38	2,537.38
12.	Value added rate	%	32,27	57,67

Conclussions and recommendations

Primary members of the vetiver oil supply chain consist of farmers, vetiver root collectors, distillers, vetiver oil collectors, and exporters. They are classified as Small Medium Enterprises (SME's) except exporters. They are located in Garut Regency, West Java and spread over in five Sub-districts namely Bayongbong, Samarang, Cilawu, Leles and Pasir Wangi, while exporters are located in Bogor, Sukabumi and Jakarta. Partnerships between farmers, distillers, collectors or exporters consist usually of long term relationships based on trust. The major problems that are faced in the vetiver supply chain are low quality and the use of simple technology. Value added of vetiver oils is in dry season higher (IDR 2,537.38/kg) than that in the wet season (IDR 887.38/kg). The difference of value added between two seasons is about 65 percent.

This study recommends further research on up-grading strategies to improve the vetiver oil supply chain and analyse the industrial risks along the chain.

Acknowledgements

The authors gratefully acknowledge the financial assistance provided by the Directorate General of Higher Education, Ministry of National Education, Republic of Indonesia through Competitive Grant for Researchers.

We also express our gratitude to the members of the vetiver supply chain (farmers, root collectors, distillers, vetiver oil collectors, and exporters), the Ministry of Industry, the Ministry of Agriculture of Republic of Indonesia and College students of the Department of Management, Faculty of Economics and Management, Bogor Agricultural University.

References

Balou, R.H.: Business Logistics/ Supply Chain Management. 5th edition. Prentice Hall New Jersey, 2004.

Chopra, S. and Meindl, P.: Supply Chain Management: Strategy, Planning and Operation. 3rd edition. Prentice Hall, New Jersey, 2007.

Fawcett, S.E, Ellram, L.M. and Ogden, J.A.: Supply Chain management: from Vision to Implementation. Prentice Hall, New Jersey, 2007.

Hayami, Y., Kawagui, T., Morooka, Y., and Siregar, M.: Agricultural Marketing and Processing in Upland Java, A Perspective From A Sunda Village. CGPRT No. 8. The CGPRT Centre, 1987.

Indrawanto, C., Kajian Pengembangan Industri Akar Wangi (*Vetiveria zizanoides L.*) Menggunakan Interpretative Structural Modelling. Informatika Pertanian 18 (1): 1-18. Pusat Penelitian dan Pengembangan Perkebunan, Bogor, 2009.

Lambert, D.M. and Cooper, M.C.: Issues in Supply Chain Management. Industrial Marketing Management. 29 (1). 65-83, 2000.

Mentzer, J.T. et al.: Defining Supply Chain Management. Journal of Business Logistics Vol 22 No.2, 2001.

Mulyati, H. A., Setiawan, S., and Rusli, M.S.: Rancang Bangun Sistem Manajemen Rantai Pasokan dan Risiko Minyak Akar Wangi Berbasis IKM di Indonesia. Lembaga Penelitian dan Pengabdian Kepada Masyarakat Institut Pertanian Bogor, Bogor, 2009.

Perera, M. Sarath, S.K. and Weeraweha, J.: Analysis of Vegetable Supply Chain of Supermarkets in Srilanka. Srilanka Journal of Agricultural Economics. Vol. 6 No.1, 2004.

Pujawan, I. Nyoman: *Supply Chain Management*. Penerbit Guna Jaya. Surabaya, 2005.

Simichi-Levi, *et al*.: Designing and Managing the Supply Chain (Concepts, Strategis, and Case Studies). International Edition. Mc. Graw-Hill, Singapore, 2000.

Yin, K., Case Study Research: Design and Methods. Sage Publications Inc., USA, 1994.

Affordable Safe Drinking Water for the Poor

Chicgoua Noubactep

Angewandte Geologie, Universität Göttingen, Goldschmidtstraße 3, D-37077, Göttingen, Germany.
Kultur und Nachhaltige Entwicklung CDD e.V., Postfach 1502, D-37005 Göttingen, Germany.
E-Mail: cnoubac@gwdg.de; Tel.: + 49 551 393191; Fax: + 49 551 399379.

"The close link between scientific research and technical invention appears to be a new factor in the nineteenth century. According to Mumford, *"the principal initiatives came, not from the inventor-engineer, but from the scientist who established the general law"*. The scientist took cognizance both of the new raw materials which were available and of the new human needs which had to be met. Then he deliberately oriented his research toward a scientific discovery that could be applied technically. And he did this out of simple curiosity or because of definite commercial and industrial demands. Pasteur, for instance, was encouraged in his bacteriological research by wine producers and silkworm growers. ...In the twentieth century, this relationship between scientific research and technical invention resulted in the enslavement of science to technique".

Jacques Ellul (1954)

Abstract

The world is on schedule to meet the Water Millennium Development Goal of halving by 2015 the proportion of people (1.1 billion) without safe drinking water in 1990. However, up to 550 million people may still lack safe drinking in 2015. Therefore, the development of efficient and affordable water treatment technologies is a challenge for the scientific community. Resulted technologies should ideally be practicable for small communities with little technological skills. Water filtration on ceramic filter and biosand filter has been identified as such a universally applicable technology. However, both filters mainly address microbial contamination but virus removal is still none satisfying. Current efforts are directed towards improving these filtration systems. This communication presents the concept of amending biosand filter with a reactive layer containing metallic iron (Fe^0 filters). Fe^0 filters have the advantage of addressing both chemical and microbial contamination. The operating mode of Fe^0 filters is explained and some research needs are discussed. It is hope that more researchers will be interested in co-developing this promising health-keeping technology in various parts of the globe.

Preamble

The concept presented in this contribution is part of efforts of the association *"Kultur und Nachhaltige Entwicklung (CDD e.V.)"* (Culture and Sustainable Development – Culture et Développement Durable) based in Göttingen (Germany). One of the goals of this cultural association is to contribute to shift the current paradigm of international development assistance by encouraging the population in need to (further) develop available concepts that may help them to solve their problems by themselves. No patented solution is presented but a flexible concept adaptable to any local situations and implicitly taking particular cultural preferences into account. The resulted technology may be low-cost for the poor. Low-cost could solely mean less money expense. "Less money expense" is the key to fight poverty.

Introduction

The availability of safe drinking water for human consumption is a crucial prerequisite for human well-being. Drinking water must be physically accessible and in sufficient quantity. Technically, water accessibility can be achieved all over the world. This goal could be met for example by (i) harvesting and storing rainwater, (ii) pumping surface water from the river, or (iii) digging and pumping water from the aquifer. Practically, however, rendering water accessible is not always affordable. This contribution is focused on water treatment, disregarding how water is made available.

The conventional approach to provide people with safe drinking water is to treat available water in waterworks and distribute clean water through a pipe system. This approach is sometimes prohibitively expensive and is never eco-friendly. Disregarding all classical drawbacks of centralized water supply systems, there are many situations in which providing small scattered communities with safe drinking water in a decentralized manner is of paramount importance. Relevant examples include small islands, remote small towns and villages. Accordingly, the development of decentralized drinking water supply systems has moved from an 'emergency solution' or 'alternative solution' to an 'appropriate stand-alone solution', not only for small communities in the developing world (Noubactep, 2010, Slaughter, 2010, Moglia et al., 2011a, Moglia et al., 2011b; Noubactep, 2011a).

There is still a popular view regarding decentralized solutions for safe drinking water provision as "low-tech" approach (Byars and Antizar-Ladislao, 2011). Considering the view of the French thinker Jacques Ellul (1954), however, solving an identified problem is a priority scientific challenge. The present communication is focused on the provision of small communities with safe drinking water. Therefore, the characteristics of these communities are discussed first.

Small communities and population in need

Small communities

There is no clear definition for a 'small community'. In Germany, a small community may be a village with less than 1,000 inhabitants. In the rainforest of Cameroon, scattered small communities rarely have up to 100 inhabitants. In oceans, small communities may be only a few hundred people on small islands surrounded by millions of square kilometres of ocean. However, either in developed or developing countries, small communities have in common their geographic remoteness and their weak financial resources (Smith Jr., 2008, Gottinger et al., 2011). In the developing countries, technological isolation, colonial history, and weak educational resources constitute significant barriers to improving access to safe drinking water (Smith Jr., 2008, Momba et al., 2009, Smith Jr., 2009).

Population in need

Identifying the population in need of safe drinking water is the best approach to solve their problems. An excellent description is given in the following paragraph from Momba et al. (2009):

"In South Africa, water infrastructure is well developed in urban areas as opposed to rural areas where the infrastructure is either poorly developed or non-existent. The supply of water to rural communities is usually undertaken through small water treatment plants (*SWTP*), defined as water treatment systems that are installed in areas which are not well serviced and which do not normally fall within the boundaries of urban areas. They include water supplies from boreholes and springs which are then chlorinated, treatment plants of small municipalities and establishments such as rural hospitals, schools, clinics and forestry stations. However, the efficacy of small water treatment plants is plagued by several technical and management problems, which include: the inability of plant operators to calculate chlorine dosages, determine flow rate, and estimate free chlorine residual concentrations, undertake readings of turbidity and pH values, or effect repairs of basic equipment. In addition, there appears to be lack of understanding of process selection, design, chlorination techniques, process quality monitoring and evaluation. Others include poor working conditions, the frequent depletion of chemical stock, lack of a maintenance culture, lack of emergency preparedness and poor communication. In addition, many of the SWTP sites are remote and secluded – this may result in limited technical support which often leads to dysfunctional disinfection systems. This is corroborated by the extensive documentation on the supply of water of poor microbiological quality, which is unsafe for human consumption, in different provinces of South Africa."

This paragraph clearly demonstrates that the population in need in developing countries is not only the rural remote one but also the peri-urban one (Rosa and Clasen, 2010). This situation demonstrates the need of appropriate technologies. In other words, appropriate technologies are needed for people: (i) lacking process understanding, (ii) unable to monitor and evaluate the treatment process, and (iii) lacking chemicals for disinfection.

Requirements to appropriate technologies

The paragraph from Momba et al. (2009) has recalled the problems of small communities in general; see also Frechen et al. (2011). The key problems are: (i) lack of an electricity grid, (ii) lack of chemicals for disinfection, (iii) lack of skilled personnel to properly use chemicals when they are available. Accordingly, an ideal technology for such a population must fulfil the following two key requirements (i) be gravity-driven (no electricity is needed) and (ii) use no chemicals for disinfection (no skilled personnel is needed). Additionally, the treatment unit must be compact (no moving parts). Any efficient technology fulfilling these requirements can be operated by everyone and is therefore appropriate.

From the available technologies, only the WaterBackpack (Frechen et al. 2011) has been reported to satisfactorily treat water without chemicals or energy. However, this Award winning micro-filtration device is patented and was designed for emergency situations (e.g. earthquakes, flooding, hurricanes, tsunami, and wars). A WaterBackpack currently costs about Euro 700 and can provide 200 to 500 people with 7 litres per person and day (Frechen et al., 2011). Since the goal of this contribution is to 'transfer' a concept (not a product) to be co-developed using locally available materials, the WaterBackpack would only be useful in emergency situations or as bridging solution for larger communities. Therefore, 'indigenous cost-effective solutions' are still needed for poor families in their small communities."

Appropriateness of available technologies

Several authors (e.g. Ali, 2010, Rosa and Clasen, 2010, Michen, 2011) recently discussed the suitability of available technologies for the provision of low-skilled people with safe drinking water. They came to the univocal conclusion, that filtration is the only technology fulfilling the requirements discussed earlier (see section 3). Accordingly, there are intensive efforts to improve both ceramic filtration and biosand filtration. For example, Michen (2011) presented some approaches to understand and improve the efficiency of ceramic filter candles for virus removal. On the other hand several research groups are currently testing the possibility to amend biosand filters with metallic iron (Fe^0) to improve their efficiency to remove pathogen, including viruses (Kim et al., 2011, Shi et al., 2012).

Inherent difficulty of filtration for treatment of multi-component systems

In filtration, the primary contaminant removal mechanism is based on size-exclusion or sieving using billions of sites distributed in a porous bed (Holdich, 2002). Basically, for each contaminant a proper filtration medium (e.g. an adsorbent) must be found that offers effective capture and immobilization. The filtration medium is ideally able to be re-used upon regeneration. However, natural water usually contains several microbial and chemical contaminants of various chemical and physical intrinsic properties. The difficulty arises from the constraint to simultaneously remove dissolved or suspended contaminants with antagonistic properties (e.g. large/small, polar/non-polar, charged/neutral).

The current prevailing paradigm is summarized by Doula (2009) as follows: "there is no one piece of treatment equipment that manages all contaminants. All treatment methods have limitations. The treatment system that is best for any particular situation (rural or municipal water system, household, industry, well, underground, irrigation, etc.) depends on the contaminant(s) present, concentration(s), size of equipment and maintenance and operational requirements of the system. There also may be situations in which a combination of treatment methods is most effective. An example of this is the use of a sediment filter as pre-treatment before activated carbon treatment".

The current state-of-the-art knowledge on the process of aqueous contaminant removal in the presence of Fe^0 challenges this view as highlighted in the next section.

Contaminant removal in Fe⁰ beds

Volumetric expansive nature of Fe⁰ oxidation at pH > 4.5
At pH values > 4.5, the solubility of Fe is very low, therefore iron will spontaneously precipitate from aqueous solutions (Noubactep, 2011b). Accordingly, Fe^0 oxidation by water yields Fe^{II}/Fe^{III} hydroxides and oxides (precipitates) which are good adsorbents for several groups of biological and chemical contaminants. In fact, Fe oxide beds and Fe oxide-coated sand have been extensively used as filtration media in water treatment (Gutierrez et al., 2009, Wei et al., 2010). However, Fe oxides are specific for the removal of charged species.

The suitability of Fe^0 as universal filtration medium for safe drinking water provision arises from the fact that Fe^0 corrosion occurs in-situ (Noubactep et al., 2009, Noubactep, 2011a). During this process, very reactive colloids are generated and further transformed in the presence of traces amounts of contaminants (Henderson and Demond, 2011, Kümmerer, 2011). These contaminants are enmeshed in the mass of precipitating Fe^{II}/Fe^{III} hydroxides without necessarily having any specific affinity to iron hydroxides. This dynamic process occurs billion of times at different depths in a Fe^0 bed, improving size-exclusion which is the basic mechanism of contaminant removal in filtration system.

Each Fe atom (Fe^0) is first oxidized to Fe^{2+}, Fe^{2+} is then hydrolysed to $[Fe\,(H_2O)_6]^{2+}$. $[Fe(H_2O)_6]^{2+}$ may be oxidized to $[Fe(H_2O)_6]^{3+}$. $[Fe(H_2O)_6]^{2+/3+}$ is polymerised to large colloids which are then transformed to hydroxides ($Fe(OH)_2$ and $Fe(OH)_3$) upon dehydration. Fe hydroxides are further transformed to more crystalline Fe oxides.

Considering the volumetric changes, each Fe^0 atom first experiences an expansion (Fe^0 to colloids) and then a compression (colloids to hydroxide or oxide). The net balance is an expansion Fe^0 to hydroxide or oxide. It is well-known that the volume of the corrosion product is higher than that of the original metal (Pilling and Bedworth, 1923). In the case Fe^0, the ratio between the volume of corrosion products (V_{oxide}) and the volume of the parent metal (V_{metal}) is called "rust expansion coefficient" ($\eta = V_{oxide}/V_{metal}$; $2.1 \leq \eta \leq 6.40$) (Caré et al., 2008).

Contaminant removal in Fe⁰ beds: reactive filtration

The mechanisms of contaminant removal in a Fe^0 beds are: (i) adsorption mostly onto Fe corrosion products, (ii) co-precipitation with nascent Fe corrosion products, and (iii) size-exclusion (straining). Clearly, beside adhesion (adsorption) by several mechanisms (sedimentation on bed solids, electrostatic attraction or repulsion, inertia), contaminants are enmeshed in the mass of Fe corrosion products and/or are strained from the solution due to size-exclusion.

It is very important to stress the fact that the dynamic cycle of expansion/contraction accompanying the process of iron oxidation and precipitation acts as contaminant collector. In this manner even very small contaminants (e.g. viruses) which may have passed through a conventional filter of similar pore size, are 'swept' by transforming colloids. This collection mechanism, termed as reactive filtration (Noubactep 2010), is the reason for the universal suitability of Fe^0 beds for safe drinking water provision. For the realization of this goal, all is needed is a proper bed design.

Design of Fe⁰ beds

The increase in volume associated with aqueous iron corrosion ($2.1 \leq \eta \leq 6.40$ – section 4.2.1) necessarily induces a progressive occupation of the initial porosity by in-situ generated expansive Fe species. This process leads to a progressive loss of porosity that is coupled to a loss of hydraulic conductivity (permeability loss). Therefore, permeability loss is inherent to Fe^0 beds. The challenge is to find a balance between efficient contaminant removal and sustained permeability. It should be noticed that pure Fe^0 beds were very efficient but not sustainable (Hussam and Munir, 2007; Hussam, 2009). On the other hand, SONO filters, designed for arsenic removal are currently removing all classes of contaminants from water in rural Nepal and Bangladesh (Noubactep, 2011a). SONO filters should be regarded as first-generation efficient Fe^0-based filtration systems for decentralized safe drinking water provision. The heart of SONO filters is a proprietary porous composite iron material.

Because replacing a fraction of Fe^0 in a Fe^0 filter by other materials of comparable particle size will not impact the initial porosity, the first tool for a sustainable Fe^0 bed is to diminish the proportion of Fe^0. An inert material (e.g. gravel, pumice, sand) or a reactive but non expansive material (e.g. MnO_2) can be used. As Fe^0 is a generator of 'contaminant collectors' (section 4.2.2), the challenge the challenge comes down to finding out the amount of Fe^0 that could efficiently sustain contaminant removal in media filtration. Using sand as reference medium for filtration, it is clear that what is needed is a Fe^0-amended sand filter. This means that sand is the main filtration media (volumetric abundance) while Fe^0 is added to sustain the efficiency of sand filters (Noubactep et al., 2010).

Accordingly, the challenge for the scientific community is to find out a correlation between (i) water quality, (ii) water flow rate through the filter, (iii) dimensions of the filter (section, length), (iv) intrinsic Fe^0 reactivity, and (v) thickness of the reactive layer and the proportion of Fe^0 therein for efficient contaminant removal.

The science of Fe^0 filters

People familiar to the technology of using Fe^0 as reactive medium in subsurface permeable reactive barriers (O'Hannesin and Gillham, 1998, Henderson and Demond, 2007, Comba et al., 2011, Ghauch et al., 2011, Gheju, 2011) may wonder why Fe^0 is not presented as a reducing agent. However, considering Fe^0 as a reducing agent has been a mistake (Noubactep, 2011b, 2011c, 2012 and references cited therein). This mistake has confused a part of the scientific community. It should be recalled here, that chemical reduction is not a removal mechanism, accordingly, even reduced species must be removed from water to obtain potable water.

Some isolated researchers have intentionally used Fe^0 as colloid generators for contaminant removal (Khan et al., 2000, Karschunke, 2005). This approach is rationalized for example by the study of Pokhrel and Viraraghavan (2009) who found that in column studies, an iron to arsenic ratio of 40:1 was necessary to ensure an effluent arsenic concentration of 5 mg/L or lower. These findings are in agreement with the historical concept presented by Yao et al. (1971) that collectors are necessary to improve the efficiency of sand filters.

The author of the present article has developed a sound concept for safe drinking water provision at small-scale (Noubactep et al., 2009, Noubactep et al., 2012) which is yet to be realized. Interested researchers should not care about existing patents since these are based on a false premise. Some of these patents are even posterior to the original concept presented in Noubactep et al. (2009). Most of the patents addressed only a group of contaminants (e.g. pathogen removal, pesticides).

The fact that so many patents exist based on a false premise is a jeopardy for science as a whole. With regard on the international development assistance, false patented processes could be imported in countries with citizens of outstanding ability. However, the colonial history has reduced them to 'disabled' consumers of 'international assistance'. It is hoped that this contribution and related papers, will encourage people from various ethnicity to contribute to solve a long lasting problem at local level.

Concluding remarks

Over the past 18 years (from 1994 on) there have been several journal articles, academic thesis, textbooks and book chapters authored on several aspects of using metallic iron (Fe^0) for water treatment. Accordingly, there is no lack of information about the Fe^0/H_2O system, but rather a plethora. The question is where to start off? This contribution was conceived as a starting point for researchers/students new to the subject and particularly interested in co-developing Fe^0 filters for safe drinking water provision at small scale (household, small community). Beside the author's related articles, interested readers are encouraged to read an online available book from Holdich (2002) (http://www.particles.org.uk/ particle_technology_book) to understand the nature of filtration on Fe^0 beds (deep-bed filtration). Beside the content of this textbook, solid knowledge of the Darcy's low will be necessary.

The currently tested design of Fe^0 filters is built on the idea of one Fe^0 filter sandwiched between two fine sand filters. The first fine sand filter acts as a conventional biosand filter removing pathogen and dissolved O_2 from water. Aqueous chemical contaminants and residual pathogens are removed in the Fe^0 filter and dissolved Fe from the Fe^0 filter is removed in the second fine sand filter. Depending on the results of this design, locally available bio-/geomaterials could be added in the first or the second fine sand filter. The optimal proportions could be designed in a single compact filter for simplicity.

The last important aspect will be to revive approaches to produce iron at local level. Before optimal 'indigenous irons' (including iron composites) are made available, researchers are encouraged to test readily available Fe^0-bearing materials as steel wool, construction steel, iron nails. There is no doubt that Fe^0 filters will soon improve the health of people in many corners of the globe.

References

Ali, S. I.: Alternatives for safe water provision in urban and peri-urban slums. Journal of Water and Health 8, 720–734, 2010.

Byars, P. and Antizar-Ladislao, B.: Water treatment and supply: intermediate education in Sub-Saharan Africa. Water Science & Technology: Water Supply 11, 578–585, 2011.

Caré, S., Nguyen, Q. T., L'Hostis, V. and Berthaud, Y.: Mechanical properties of the rust layer induced by impressed current method in reinforced mortar. Cement and Concrete Research 38, 1079–1091, 2008.

Comba, S., Di Molfetta, A., Sethi, R.: A Comparison between field applications of nano-, micro-, and millimetric zero-valent iron for the remediation of contaminated aquifers. Water, Air, & Soil Pollution 215, 595–607, 2011.

Doula, M. K.: Simultaneous removal of Cu, Mn and Zn from drinking water with the use of clinoptilo-lite and its Fe-modified form. Water Research 43, 3659–3672, 2009.

Ellul, J.: *The technological society*. New York: Vintage Books. cited by Smith Jr. (2009) , 1964.

Frechen, F. B., Exler, H., Romaker, J. and Schier, W.: Long-term behaviour of a gravity-driven dead end membrane filtration unit for potable water supply in cases of disasters. Water Science & Technology: Water Supply 11, 39–44, 2011.

Ghauch, A., Abou Assi, H., Baydoun, H., Tuqan, A. M. and Bejjani, A.: Fe^0-based trimetallic systems for the removal of aqueous diclofenac: Mechanism and kinetics. Chemical Engineering Journal 172, 1033–1044, 2011.

Gheju, M.: Hexavalent chromium reduction with zero-valent iron (ZVI) in aquatic systems. Water, Air, & Soil Pollution 222, 103–148, 2011.

Gottinger, A. M., McMartin, D. W., Price, D. and Hanson B.: The effectiveness of slow sand filters to treat Canadian rural prairie water. Canadian Journal of Civil Engineering 38, 455–463, 2011.

Gutierrez, L., Li X., Wang, J., Nangmenyi, G., Economy, J., Kuhlenschmidt, T. B., Kuhlenschmidt, M. S. and Nguyen, T. H.: Adsorption of rotavirus and bacteriophage MS2 using glass fiber coated with hematite nanoparticles. Water Research 43, 5198–5208, 2009.

Henderson, A. D. and Demond, A. H.: Long-term performance of zero-valent iron permeable reactive barriers: a critical review. Environmental Engineering Science 24, 401–423, 2007.

Henderson, A. D. and Demond, A. H.: Impact of solids formation and gas production on the permeability of ZVI PRBs. Journal of Environmental Engineering 137, 689–696, 2011.

Holdich, R. G.: Fundamentals of particle technology. Shepshed: Midland Information Technology and Publishing, 173 p., 2002.

Hussam, A. and Munir, A. K. M.: A simple and effective arsenic filter based on composite iron matrix: Development and deployment studies for groundwater of Bangladesh. Journal of Environmental Science and Health Part A 42, 1869–1878, 2007.

Hussam, A.: Contending with a Development Disaster: SONO Filters Remove Arsenic from Well Water in Bangladesh. Innovations 4, 89–102, 2009.

Karschunke, K.: Nutzung der Eisenkorrosion zur Entfernung von Arsen aus Trinkwasser. Dissertation, Technische Universität Berlin, 170 Seiten, 2005.

Khan, A. H., Rasul, S. B., Munir, A. K. M., Habibuddowla, M., Alauddin, M., Newaz, S. S. and Hussam, A.: Appraisal of a simple arsenic removal method for groundwater of Bangladesh. Journal of Environmental Science and Health Part A 35, 1021–1041, 2000.

Kim, J. Y., Lee, C., Love, D. C., Sedlak, D. L., Yoon, J. and Nelson, K. L.: Inactivation of MS2 coliphage by ferrous ion and zero-valent iron nanoparticles, Environmental Science & Technology 44, 6978–6984, 2011.

Kümmerer, K.: Emerging contaminants versus micro-pollutants. Clean – Soil, Air, Water 39, 889–890, 2011.

Michen, B.: Virus removal in ceramic depth filters: The electrostatic enhanced adsorption approach. PhD Dissertation, Technische Universität Bergakademie Freiberg (Germany) , 2011.

Moglia, M., Alexander, K. S. and Sharma, A.: Discussion of the enabling environments for decentralised water systems. Water Science & Technology 63, 2331–2339, 2011a.

Moglia, M., Sharma, A., Alexander, K. and Mankad, A.: Perceived performance of decentralised water systems: a survey approach. Water Science & Technology: Water Supply 11, 516–526, 2011b.

Momba, M. N. B., Obi, C. L. and Thompson, P.: Survey of disinfection efficiency of small drinking water treatment plants: Challenges facing small water treatment plants in South Africa. Water SA 35, 485–494, 2009.

Noubactep, C., Schöner, A. and Woafo, P.: Metallic iron filters for universal access to safe drinking water. Clean: Soil, Air, Water 37, 930–937, 2009.

Noubactep, C.: Metallic iron for safe drinking water worldwide. Chemical Engineering Journal 165, 740–749, 2010.

Noubactep, C., Caré, S., Togue-Kamga, F., Schöner, A. and Woafo, P.: Extending service life of household water filters by mixing metallic iron with sand. Clean – Soil, Air, Water 38, 951–959, 2010.

Noubactep, C.: Metallic iron for safe drinking water production, *Freiberg Online Geology* 27, 38 pp, ISSN 1434-7512. (www.geo.tu-freiberg.de/fog) , 2011a.

Noubactep, C.: Aqueous contaminant removal by metallic iron: Is the paradigm shifting? Water SA 37, 419–426, 2011b.

Noubactep, C.: Metallic iron for water treatment: A knowledge system challenges mainstream science. Fresenius Environmental Bulletin 20, 2632–2637, 2011c.

Noubactep, C.: Investigating the processes of contaminant removal in Fe^0/H_2O systems. The Korean Journal of Chemical Engineering (accepted 2011/12/15), 2012.

Noubactep, C., Caré, S., Btatkeu, K. B. D. and Nanseu-Njiki, C. P.: Enhancing the sustainability of household Fe^0/sand filters by using bimetallics and MnO_2. Clean Soil Air Water, doi: 10.1002/clen.201100014, 2012.

O'Hannesin, S. F. and Gillham, R. W.: Long-term performance of an in situ "iron wall" for remediation of VOCs. Ground Water 36, 164–170, 1998.

Pilling, N. B. and Bedworth, R. E.: The oxidation of metals at high temperatures. Journal of the Institute of Metals 29, 529–591, 1923.

Pokhrel, D. and Viraraghavan, T.: Biological filtration for removal of arsenic from drinking water. Journal of Environmental Management 90, 1956–1961, 2009.

Rosa, G. and Clasen, T.: Estimating the scope of household water treatment in low- and medium-income countries. The American Journal of Tropical Medicine and Hygiene 82, 289–300, 2010.

Shi, C., Wei, J., Jin, Y., Kniel, K. E. and Chiu, P. C.: Removal of viruses and bacteriophages from drinking water using zero-valent iron. Separation and Purification Technology 84, 72–78, 2012.

Slaughter, S.: Improving the sustainability of water treatment systems: Opportunities for innovation. Solutions 1, 42–49, 2010.

Smith, Jr. W. J.: The place of rural, remote and least-wealthy small islands in international water development: the nexus of geography–technology sustainability in Chuuk State, Federated States of Micronesia. The Geographical Journal 174, 251–268, 2008.

Smith, Jr. W. J.: Geographic research in water resources: a vibrant research agenda for the next 20 years. Journal of Contemporary Water Research & Education 142, 83–89, 2009.

Wei, J., Kniel, K., Sims, J. T. and Jin, Y.: Virus' (MS2, φ174, and Aichi) attachment on sand measured by atomic force microscopy and their transport through sand columns. Environmental Science & Technology 44, 2426–2432, 2010.

Yao, K.-M., Habibian, M. T. and O'melia, C. R.: Water and waste water filtration: concepts and applications. Environmental Science & Technology 5, 1105–1112, 1971.

Added Value Analysis and Performance Improvement Strategy on Vegetable Supply Chain in Indonesia

Alim Setiawan S and Heti Mulyati

Department of Management, Faculty of Economy and Management, Institut Pertanian Bogor
Kampus IPB Darmaga, Bogor 16680, E-Mail : alimss@ipb.ac.id, heti_mulyati@yahoo.com

Abstract

One of the crucial problems in the vegetable supply chain is the low added-value of vegetables produced by farmers. This is shown by the unfair distribution of income and added value obtained by farmers compared with other actors of the vegetable supply chain. The research aims to: (1) analyse the vegetable supply chain, (2) analyse the added value of each of the actors in the vegetable supply chain, and (3) formulate a strategy to enhance added value of vegetables farmers in the supply chain. The results of analysis show that the percentage of added value at farmers is smaller than that of the other actors. Added value products at farmers range between 5.46 percent and 24.92 percent, while that of the processor between 6.51 percent and 64.85 percent, and retailers between 31.33 percent and 68.57 percent. The percentage of farmer's added value will be greater with the transfer of partial product processing activities, improving the quality and effectiveness of the institutional role of the farmer. The Strengths, Weaknesses, Opportunities and Threath (SWOT) strategy analysis leads to the following recommendations to improve the performance: (1) use hydrophonic cultivation technology and reduce excessive pesticides, (2) optimizing planting and harvesting schedules according to the climate; (3) increase the responsiveness and the flexibility in meeting with consumer orders, and (4) implement the required standard quality assurance and management systems to ensure the consistency of the product quality and acceptability by the global consumers.

Introduction

Horticulture in Indonesia plays an important role in the agricultural sector. The trend of demand for vegetables, fruits, and flowers has been increasing. Table 1 shows the contribution of horticulture to GDP from 2000 to 2005 at constant prices. The demand for vegetables has increased with increasing population of Indonesia. Vegetable producers have to increase their production to meet the increasing demand for vegetables. Total vegetable production in Indonesia increased from 7,418,070 tons in 2000 to 9,423,011 tons in 2006 (Central Bureau Statistics, 2007).

Indonesia has a land area of 1,919,440 km^2 of which 16.3 percent is used as arable and permanent cropland (1998) (MOA, 2006b). Just 15.3 percent of cropland is irrigated (1999) (Wikipedia, 2007b; Earth Trends, 2007). The climate and history of Indonesia has resulted in lowlands (< 200 m) dominated by rice, maize, cassava, fruit and estate crops, and highlands (> 800m) dominated by vegetables and other cool-climate crops. In recent years, cropping has diversified in the meson-production areas (201-800 m) and the lowlands, with more production of vegetables, and about 30 percent of the industry in the highlands. In total, 1.1 million ha are used for vegetables and potato (MOA, 2007b). Production sectors can be further differentiated according to wet-season and dry- season cropping, distance from market, and extent of commercialization (Darmawan and Pasandaran, 2000). Vegetable production is highest in the dry season in March to April (harvested before the wet season of July-August), and lowest in the hottest part of the rainy season, when prices are consequently higher (Darmawan and Pasandaran, 2000).

Table 1. The contribution of horticulture to GDP in 2000 – 2008 at to constant prices

Horticulture Commodities	GDP (Billion IDR)								
	2000	2001	2002	2003	2004	2005	2006	2007	2008
Fruits	19,079	19,951	22,119	21,149	22,740	22,460	35,448	42,362	42,660
Vegetables	13,145	13,786	13,550	15,404	15,336	16,395	24,694	25,587	27,423
Bio pharmacy	364	383	384	423	534	2,007	3,762	4,105	4,118
Flowers	2,746	2,886	2,622	3,370	3,406	3,334	4,734	4,741	6,091

Source: Directorate General of Horticulture, 2010

The practices of vegetable production in Indonesia have not been efficient yet so that the products cannot compete in the global market. The strategy to win the global competition should include the enhancement of cooperation between business partners and the all-out effort to meet the customer demands. Efficient supply chain management should be performed in the vegetable business to integrate processes from the receiving of raw material to the selling of finished products. Vegetable supply chain management links the management of the entire set of production, manufacturing, transformations, distribution and marketing of the required products.

The major problem faced by perishable vegetable products is that they have a long supply chain. The quality of the products may decrease significantly along the chain and the income margin between actors is not distributed fairly. Farmers usually receive the lowest portion, while the traders get the highest. While market information is the key input when making decisions, farmers in the developing countries as smallholders have insufficient access to it and therefore have weak bargaining power (Vorst, 2000). The supply chain needs to set a fair amount of profit for each member. To do this, it needs to analyse the total performance of the supply chain including the added value of each member to know the distribution of profit along the chain.

Optimal supply chain design can be distinguished for each supply chain, depending on the strategy of competition and market characteristics of products and production. Performance measurement aims to support performance evaluation and determines the next steps at the level of strategy, tactics and operations (Van der Vorst, 2006). In this research, we studied the structure and profile of vegetable supply chain management, and then we analysed the added value and performance in each member of the chain. Finally, we recommended ways to improve the supply chain performance. Thus this study is expected to be beneficial not only for the company in improving its competitiveness associated with the fulfilment of consumer needs in quality, quantity and delivery time but also for the farmer groups involved.

130

Research Methods

Vegetable supply chain management is a complex system that needs to be carefully investigated. An objective oriented, holistic and effective approach, i.e. a system's approach was used in this research. Expert surveys were conducted to gain the knowledge and insight related to the supply chain management. Discussion with the stakeholders was used to acquire practical knowledge as well as the daily practice of the respected topics.

Location and Period of the Study

The study of the vegetables supply chain was conducted in West Java as one of the central areas of vegetables growers in Indonesia and Jakarta as the centre of traders and exporters. The study was conducted from the last quarter of 2008 to the last quarter of 2010. The location of the study was limited in West Java, to Bogor, Cianjur, Bandung and Garut districts, which represent centres of production of vegetables and to Jakarta. Stakeholders interviewed included farmers, farmer's groups/cooperatives, processors (Saung Mirwan Co), traders/distributors, retailers, and end customers. Some of the interviewed processors, distributors and exporters were located in Jakarta.

Data Collection and Sampling Techniques

Data and information as well as knowledge used for analysing the existing horticulture supply chain in Indonesia were collected from secondary and primary data. Secondary data were collected from Indonesia Central Bureau of Statistics, Ministry of Agriculture and Ministry of Trade, Ministry of Industry and from relevant research reports. Primary data were collected through interviews, focus group discussions and expert surveys. Sampling was done by purposive sampling with the judgments and quota sampling. The sample also considered the location, status, and sustainability business. Respondents consisted of farmers (20 persons), collectors (5 persons), processors (3 persons) and retail businesses (1 person).

Data Analysis

Data analysis was done by using descriptive analysis, Hayami method added value analysis, Data Envelopment Analysis (DEA) and SWOT analysis (Strengths, Weaknesses, Opportunities, and Threats).

Descriptive Analysis

The research was started with the selection of vegetables that would be analysed. One or a group of specific products were selected based on some criteria, such as volume, value, and types of partnership, government priority as well as the internal and external factors of the commodities and products development. Each of the selected products was then carefully studied according to conceptual supply chain research framework developed by Van der Vorst et al. (2005) and Lambert and Cooper (2000). Four main aspects were investigated, i.e., chain structure and boundary, chain business process, network and chain management, and chain resources.

Added Value Analysis

Added value is the difference between input costs and output value. The added value along the supply chain can be tangible goods added and intangible services supplied (Hines, 2004). Added value is all the additional value created at a certain stage by production factors, including tangible added value through the transformation of raw materials, labour and capital goods, as well as intangible added value through intellectual capital (use of knowledge assets) and an exchange relationship (i.e. building cooperative relationship). According to Hayami et al. (1987), tangible added value is influenced by technical factors (production capacity, amount of raw materials used and labour) and market factors (output price, wage of labour, raw materials prices, and value of other inputs), which can be formulated as follows:

$$\text{Added-value-} = f\{K, B, T, U, H, h, L\} \text{ where,} \qquad (1)$$

K = production capacity; B = used raw materials; T = labour; U = Wage labour; H = output price; h = raw materials price; L = value of other *inputs* (value and all the sacrifices that occurred during the process to add value)

Supply Chain Performance Analysis

Supply chain performance is the overall performance measure that depends on the performance of the supply chain stages (Chopra and Meindl, 2001). Different methods exist that can incorporate multiple performance indicators into one measurement system. One of the best known is Data Envelopment Analysis-DEA (Aramyan et al., 2006). DEA is a mathematical programming technique that calculates the relative efficiencies of multiple DMUs based on multiple inputs and outputs. DEA measures the relative efficiency of each Decision Making Units (DMU) in comparison to other DMUs. An efficiency score of a DMU is generally defined as the weighted sum of outputs divided by the weighted sum of inputs, while weights need to be assigned. DEA model computes weights that give the highest possible relative efficiency score to a DMU while keeping the efficiency scores of all DMUs less than or equal to 1 under the same set of weights (Wong and Wong, 2007). The basic model of DEA (Zhaohan et al. 1996, Zhang, Liu, and Li, 2002 and Wong and Wong, 2007) is:

$$\text{Maximum efficiency:} \quad \eta_k = \frac{\sum U_r \, Y_{rk}}{\sum V_i \, X_{ik}} \qquad (2)$$

Where
k = decision making units (DMU)
U_r = weight of output r
V_i = weight of input i
Y_{rk} = value of output r of DMU k
X_{ik} = value of input i of DMU k

SWOT analysis is a way to identify factors in a systematic way in order to formulate improvement strategy. This analysis is based on the logic in order to maximizing Strengths and Opportunities but at the same time minimize Weaknesses and Threats. SWOT analysis in order to obtain more precise decisions can be made through stages as follows (Marimin, 2004): evaluate external and internal factors, making the external and internal SWOT matrix, and decision-making.

Study Results

Vegetable Supply Chain

Vegetable supply chain structure is generally composed of farmers, dealers, cooperatives, processors, (Saung Mirwan Co), hotels suppliers, restaurants, supermarkets, exporters, and retailers. Physical flow of vegetable products runs from farmers/farmer groups who send them to the processor to be sorted and packaged, shipped to the retailer and then sold to consumers or sent to hotels and restaurants for further processing. On the contrary, finances and information flow from the consumer, retailer, hotels and restaurants to the processor, then from the processor to the farmers/farmer groups (Figure 1).

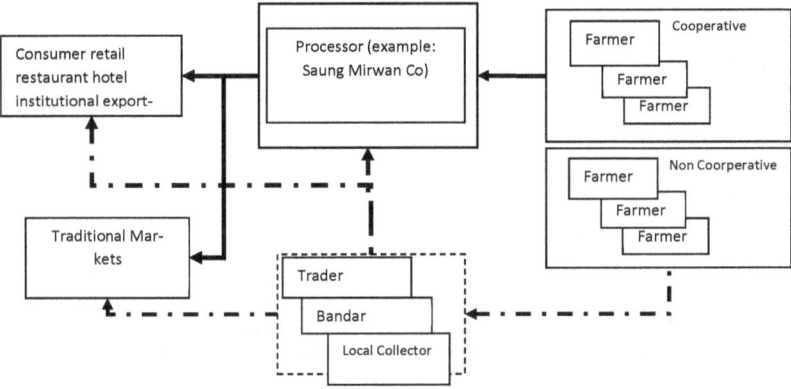

Figure 1. Vegetable supply chain in West Java, Indonesia

Chain structure

The processor (Saung Mirwan Co) processes vegetables supplied from its own farms and from their farmer's partner farms located around the company. Saung Mirwan receives, sorts/grades, packages, stores and distributes the products. Partnership between Saung Mirwan and farmer partners or buyer partners is based on trust and transparency. Saung Mirwan informs the farmers about the quantity and quality of demand, market target, and price of products. All of the crops from farmers will be bought by Saung Mirwan but it depends to standardization of quality for each product. A product that is not appropriate to the agreed standard will be rejected. This is a farmer risk. The partnership objectives are to increase and guarantee products supply from farmers, to increase farmer's skills on cultivating crop and to increase farmers' income and welfare. On the other hand, the partnership between processor and retailer –supermarket and restaurant- is based on yearly agreements.

Retailers determine a product's quality and quantity. The price determination is based on market condition.

After harvesting, the vegetables are washed directly then delivered to the processor (Saung Mirwan Co) by farmer partners. The processor then sorts, grades and packs the products according to the quality standard. Fresh cut vegetables are vacuum packed to preserve the quality for a longer time, while fresh vegetables are packed in plastics. The packed products are tagged with "Fresh & Quality" label. The price of other fresh cut vegetables is more expensive than the price of fresh vegetables. Post-harvest activities of the vegetable chain are shown in Table 2.

Table 2. Post-Harvest Activities in Vegetable Supply Chain

Activities	Done by		
	Farmer	Processor	Retailer
Harvesting and pre- handling	X		
Transportation from farmer to company	X		
Sorting and grading		X	
Packaging		X	
Labelling		X	
Transportation from company to consumer		X	
Quality control			X
Credit to consumer (in 2 days)	X	X	
Giving seeds to farmer		X	

Chain Management

In the vegetable supply chain, Saung Mirwan Co acts as processor and distributor. Saung Mirwan Co acts as the middleman that relates between farmer and market. As the processor, Saung Mirwan Co sorts, grades, assures and controls the product quality, packs, stores, transports and distributes the products to consumers. In order to get reliable suppliers, partners are selected according to the certain criteria. The main criteria for suppliers (farmer-partner of Saung Mirwan) are land availability, quality of products, price of products, experience and reputation as well as the ability to fulfill the contract agreement.

Chain Business Processes

The processor gives some support to the farmers, such as training, market information sharing and extension services, meanwhile financial credit support is still limited. Processor and farmers do a collaborative planning on planting schedule of vegetables. The processor determines the volume of production based on customers demand. The cultivation area required to be cultivated by the farmer and the amount of seeds that is given to the farmer is determined based on production volume. Meetings between processor and farmers are held if required.

Chain Resources

Physical resources: the processor gives only the seeds to the farmers. The farmers partners provide their own or rented lands for cultivation. The farmers also provide fertilizer, pesticides, and irrigation facilities themselves. *Technology*: The technology for vegetables cultivation used by the farmers is conventional. They do not use machinery equipment for their cultivation. The human resources do planting and land fertilization manually. *Human resources:* The number of workers/farmers who participate in the supply chain at every location varies. For example, vegetable farmers in Bogor, each farmer group consists of 10 – 15 persons. *Financial*: There is no financial assistance that can be accessed by farmers. The processor does not provide cash capital to the farmers (example; for renting the land). He only gives the seeds. Moreover, there is limited assistance from the government. Farmers must provide their own capital for this business. However, there is a possibility for farmers to borrow money from the coop.

Value Analysis of Vegetable Supply Chain

The added value concept is an increased value that occurs because of the input is treated on a commodity. The added value can be produced by increasing the process value or by increasing the price value. The collected data for the analysis of the added value of each supply chain member was processed using Hayami method. The added value of each vegetable supply chain member are varies, ranging from farmers to the retail level. The analysis results of added value in the supply chain actors indicate the percentage of farmers added value is still smaller (5.55 % - 24.92 %) compared to the processor (6.51 % - 64.85 %) and retail (29.60 % - 68.57 %). That farmer's percentage added value will be increasing if the transaction done through institutional cooperatives/farmer groups and the transfer of some post-harvest processing activities to farmers. Tables 3 and 4 show the results of added value analysis in Pepper and Lettuce supply chain.

Table 3. A. Chain: Cooperative Farmer – Cooperative - Retail

No.	Actors	Input prices / kg (IDR)	Other input costs / kg (IDR)	Output price / kg (IDR)	Added value / kg (IDR)	Percentage of added value (%)
		A. Chain: Cooperatives Farmer - Cooperatives - Retail				
1.	Farmer	1600	1556	8244	5088	24.92
2.	Cooperative	8244	127	9700	1329	6.51
3.	Retail	9700	300	24 000	14 000	68.57
	Number of A				20 417	100.00
		B. Chain: Farmer - Dealer - Retail				
1.	Farmer	1600	1400	7000	4000	19.38
2.	Trader/Local Collector	7000	55	10 000	2945	14.26
3.	Retail	10 000	300	24 000	13 700	66.36
	Number of B				20 645	100.00

Table 4. Added value distribution in Lettuce supply chain

No.	Actors	Input prices / kg (IDR)	Other input costs / kg (IDR)	Output price / kg (IDR)	Added value / kg (IDR)	Percentage of added value (%)
1.	Farmer	2000	500	3000	500	5.55
2.	Saung Mirwan Co	3000	1160	10 000	5840	64.85
3.	Retail	10 000	210	12 875	2665	29.60
	Number				9005	100.00

In the vegetable supply chain, farmers must have a high productivity to fulfil the customers' need. The farmers' productivity influences the productivity of processor. The processor provided the farmers with technical advices to improve their productivity and to avoid loss. The coordinator of the partnership division visited each farmer during planting periods to see that the supply of water and production facilities were sufficient. When there were not enough water and production facilities, the farmers were advised not to plant the seeds.

A supply chain will survive and grow when the profits of its members are attractively high. Vegetable supply chain in Indonesia suffered bad performance. In 2009-2010, the farmer had less of added value. To remedy this condition the profit and risk sharing among the supply chain members in the vegetable supply chain must be adjusted. One way is to increase the price of the commodity based on quality and order fulfilment. This will motivate the farmers to increase their product quality and productivity.

Performance Measurement using Data Envelopment Analysis

The performance measurement was conducted in two semesters using DEA method. There were two measurements to evaluate the DMUs (Decision Making Unit): financial and operational measures. Financial measures comprise revenue and cost. Operational measures comprise delivery reliability (on-time delivery, quality, quantity), responsiveness (cycle time), and flexibility. In this research, the only operational measurement conducted was supply chain reliability, while other measures were assumed to be the same. DEA method has two objectives i.e. minimum input and maximum output. Based on the results of the design of performance measurement model by adapting the SCOR model, then the input variables used for evaluating the vegetable supply chain performance metrics include order fulfilment lead time, cycle time of the fulfilment of orders, supply chain flexibility, cost SCM, cash-to-cash cycle time, inventory days of supply. While the output variables consist of delivery, order fulfilment and compliance with quality standards.

The results of calculation of DEA can provide performance information of six farmer partners of Saung Mirwan Co in two semesters. Lowest relative efficiency achieved by farmer A (53.43 percent) in semester 1 and farmer B (54.86 percent) in semester 2, while the highest performance achieved by farmer F (83.19 percent) in semester 1 and farmer D (70.56 percent) in semester 2 (Table 5).

Table 5. Result of DEA analysis for six-farmer partner of Saung Mirwan Co in two semester (%)

Semester	Farmer A	Farmer B	Farmer C	Farmer D	Farmer E	Farmer F
Semester 1	53.43	60.70	64.77	68.85	80.04	83.19
Semester 2	63.68	54.87	68.87	70.56	63.20	69.64

Farmers' performance analysis also indicated that in the first semester Farmer A had inefficient performance because during January to June, these groups had the lowest value of the quantity fulfilment and time delivery and also bore the greatest losses compared to the other farmer groups. During the second semester, where land productivity increased, Farmer A showed efficient performances, because with a smaller number of inputs these groups could generate a larger output value compared to the other farmer groups.

The results of DEA calculations also provide potential improvement that can be done by every farmer (units) to improve its performance. For example, in Table 6 shows the potential improvement of information that can be done to improve the farmers A relative efficiency reached 100 percent in the first semester by lowering the cash to cash cycle time from 16 days to 12 days, reducing the total cost of IDR 5,100 to IDR 4,017 per kg, improving the compliance quality standards from 31 percent to 75 percent and improve the delivery performance from 36 percent to 75 percent.

Table 6. Potential improvement of Farmer A

Factor	Performance Metrics	Semester 1			Semester 2		
		Actual	Target	Potential Improvement (%)	Actual	Target	Potential Improvement (%)
Input	Cash to cash cycle time (day)	16	12.05	-24.68	16	12.75	-20.34
	Total Cost (IDR)	5100	4017.32	-21.23	6000	4248.42	-29.19
	Cycle Order Fulfilment (day)	59	60.26	2.14	60	63.73	6.21
	Lead time (day)	55	58.25	5.91	58	61.6	6.21
Output	Compliance with Standard (%)	31.51	75.32	139.05	47.35	79.66	68.23
	Order Fulfilment (%)	65.21	100.43	54.01	100	106.21	6.21
	Delivery Performance (%)	36.36	75.32	107.16	20	79.66	298.29

The effect of the increase of output value and the reduction in the number of rejects reduced the amount of losses on farmers. It could even provide them with substantial profits. The output quantity can be increased by: (a) Improving the land condition by giving optimum production facilities (fertilizer and pesticide); (b) Avoiding the seed planting in bad weather; (c) Choosing the correct type of rotation plants to maintain the land fertility; (d) Always controlling the plant growth; and (e) Harvesting at the right time. With the increasing crops production level the farmers can earn higher profits. Increased revenue can also be gained with an increase in the buying price by processor, accompanied by an increase in farmers' delivery performance.

The percentage of on-time delivery can be attained by: (i) Following the planting schedule as determined by processor; (ii) Always controlling the plant growth. The percentage of compliance with quality standard can be increased by: (i) Protecting the plants from pests and diseases that degrade the quality of vegetable; (ii) Harvesting at the right time to get the optimum quality; (iii) Placing the products in a cool place to decrease the evaporation; (iv) Delivering the commodity in less than 4 hours after harvesting; and (v) Delivering the commodity in the proper treatment or packaging to preserve the freshness and fullness of the commodity.

Benchmark analysis was performed to compare the performance of supply chain with performance targets that should be achieved (Bolstorff, 2003). Based on Table 7, the general performance of supply chain is better than SCORcard for food products. For example, the company's delivery performance reached 98.6 percent -100 percent, greater than the value at SCORcard (95.0 percent). So did the other metric values greater than the value at SCORcard.

Table 7. Benchmarking Analysis of vegetable supply chain performance

Performance Metrics	Semester 1	Semester 2	*Superior*[*]	Gap semester 1	Gap semester 2
Delivery performance	100 %	98.6%	95.0%	+ 5%	+ 3.6%
Order Fulfilment	139. 7%	109.9%	88.0%	+ 51.7%	+ 21.9%
Compliance with Quality Standard	99 %	98%	100%	- 1%	- 2%
Lead time	2 day	2 day	3 day	+1 day	+1 day
Cycle of Order Fulfilment	4 day	4 day	14 day	+ 10 day	+ 10 day
Flexibility	3 day	3 day	10 day	+26 day	+26 day
Total cost	IDR 21.890	IDR 22.185	-	-	-
Cash to cash cycle time	23 day	21 day	29 day	+ 6 day	+ 8 day
Inventory days of supply	7 day	7 day	23 day	+ 16 day	+ 16 day

*) *Food product SCORcard* (Bolstorff, 2003) **) smt = semester

Improvement Strategies in Vegetable Supply Chain

Supply chain performance improvement strategies based on in-depth analysis of the external and internal environmental condition related to vegetable supply chains. The analysis is done because those conditions directly or indirectly affect the vegetable supply chain system. Formulation of supply chain performance improvement strategy includes strategy formulation determination stage, institutional analysis and action programs formulation. SWOT analysis carried out as the basic determinant to the strategies formulation in order to increase farmer's added value in the vegetable supply chain.

The scores calculation on the IFE *(Internal Factor Evaluation)* matrix and EFE *(External Factor Evaluation)* matrix determine the coordinates of the vegetable supply chain actors position in quadrant II, which is positive for the X axis and negative for Y axis are (+0.45; -

0.45), so the strategy *(Strengths-Threats or ST)* can be chosen as an alternative strategy to increase vegetable supply chain. Strategies formulation carried out by SWOT analysis approach in Table 8.

Table 8. The alternative strategy of supply chain performance improvement

SWOT — Internal / External	Strengths	Weaknesses
	1. Vegetables product quality indicated by high numbers that meets the standards 2. High Company responsiveness on the product delivery process, seen from a short order fulfilment cycle. 3. Adequate post-harvest infrastructure and technological support. 4. Processor located near the market (consumers)	1. The distance between farmer/buyer partner and processors are far and not always using a cool truck so affected the risk of product damage. 2. Soil fertility levels are still low 3. High pesticides residue level 4. Inadequate storage process indicated by an accumulation of crates that are too high and the limited cooling space, so the stored product has highly rapid deterioration risk.
Opportunities 1. Opportunity to improve the lost order due to a weak order management *(miss opportunity)*. 2. The existence of a partnership between farmers and government support in order to boost production capacity to fulfil increased market demand. 3. The amount of market share which encouraged by increased awareness of healthy lifestyles 4. Development of cultivation technologies, storage, packaging and transportation	**SO** 1. Information systems development to support supply chain management 2. Increased institutional collaboration in the supply chain for *sharing* information, planning / scheduling of production, and increase product quality 3. Increased responsiveness and flexibility to the performance of order fulfilment 4. Development of market share through effective marketing strategy	**WO** 1. The use of environmentally friendly pesticides or vegetables cultivation technology with hydroponics 2. Use of superior quality seeds
Threats 1. The high conversion of agricultural land for settlement and other economic sectors development 2. World trade globalization and of *non-tariff barrier* issues (environmental issues) 3. Competitors from other countries arise on the domestic market. They are also capable of producing vegetables with productivity, production efficiency and better quality 4. Climate change and the threat of pests and diseases that can reduce the volume of production.	**ST** 1. Scheduling system optimization (in planting and harvesting) consider the weather aspect 2. Improved responsiveness and flexibility performance in order fulfilment 3. Implementation of quality management system (QMS) and environmental (ISO 9000 & 14000), *Hazard Analysis Critical Control Point (HACCP), Good Handling Practices,* and *Good Agricultural Practice (GAP)* are needed.	**WT** 1. Addition of transportation mode with a better cooling facilities 2. Implementation of quality and environmental management system (ISO 22000), *Hazard Analysis Critical Control Point (HACCP), Good Handling Practices,* and *Good Agricultural Practice (GAP)* are needed.

Based on the IFE-EFE results, to increase supply chain performance then an alternative strategy chosen are *strength-threats* (ST):

1. The use of hydroponic cultivation technology and the reduction of excessive use of pesticides

2. Scheduling system optimization (in planting and harvesting) considering weather aspects

3. Improved responsiveness and flexibility performance in order fulfilment

4. Implementation of quality management system (QMS) and environmental (ISO 9000 & 14000), *Hazard Analysis Critical Control Point (HACCP), Good Handling Practices,* and *Good Agricultural Practice (GAP)* are needed.

Conclusions and Recommendations

The analysis of added value in the supply chain actors indicate that the percentage of farmers added value is still smaller (5.46% - 24.92%) compared to the processor (between 6.51% - 64.85%) and retail (between 31.33 % - 68.57%). This farmer added value will be increased if they get the transaction done through cooperatives/farmer groups and the transfer of some activities to farmers post-harvest processing of vegetable products.

Based on calculations of internal and external matrix in SWOT analysis, the position of the vegetable supply chain actors are in between the Force and Threats quadrant. Thus, the vegetable supply chain performance improvement strategy that can be formulated are: (1) The use of hydroponic cultivation technology and the reduction of excessive pesticide use, (2) Scheduling system optimization (in planting and harvesting) considering the weather aspects, (3) Improvement responsiveness and flexibility performance in order fulfilment, and (4) Implementation of quality management system (QMS) and environmental (ISO 9000 & 14000), *Hazard Analysis Critical Control Point (HACCP), Good Handling Practices,* and *Good Agricultural Practice (GAP)* are needed.

The study recommends conducting further research on the supply chain decision-making model especially in fair added value, profit distribution and risk sharing among the supply chain members.

ACKNOWLEDGEMENTS

Research that produced this publication is supported in part funded by the Directorate General of Higher Education, Ministry of National Education, Republic of Indonesia through Grant Competence No. 219/SP2H/PP/DP2M/V/2009.

References

Aramyan, L., Ondersteijn C., Kooten, O. and Lansink, A. O.: Performance Indicators in Agri-Food Production Chains, Quantifying the Agri-food Supply Chain. Ondersteijn, C.J.M., Wijnands, J.H.M., Huirne, R. B. M. and Van Kooten, O. (Eds.). Spinger-Netherlands. Chapter 5: 47-64, 2006.

Austin, J. E.: Agroindustrial Project Analysis. John Hopkins University Press, USA, 1992.

Brown, J. E.: Agroindustrial Investment and Operations. Word Bank Publications, USA, 1994.

Ballou, R. H.: Business Logistic: Supply Chain Management. Fifth Edition. Pearson Prentice Hall, New Jersey, 2004.

Chopra, S. and Meindl, P.: Supply Chain Management Strategy, Planning, and operation. Prentice Hall, New Jersey, 2004.

Darmawan, D. A. and Pasandaran, E.. In: M. Ali (ed.). Dynamics of vegetable production, distribution and consumption in Asia. AVRDC Publication 00-498. Shanhua, Tainan: AVRDC. http.//www.avrdc.org/pdf/dynamics/Indonesia.pdf, 139-171, 2000.

Hayami, Y., Kawagui, T., Morooka, Y., and Siregar, M.: Agricultural Marketing and Processing in Upland Java A Perspective From A Sunda Village. CGPRT No. 8. The CGPRT Centre, 1987.

Lambert, D. M. and Cooper, M. C. : Issues in Supply Chain Management. Industrial Marketing Management. 29 (1), 65-83, 2000.

Marimin, Slamet, A. S., Maghfiroh, N. and Astuti, R.: Country Report: Supply Chains for Perishables Agricultural Products in Indonesia. Asian Productivity Organization (APO) Research on Supply Chains in Agribusiness. Tokyo, 2008.

MOA. Ministry of Agriculture, Republic of Indonesia: http://www.deptan.go.id/ 2007.

Pujawan, I. N.: Supply Chain Management. Penerbit Guna Jaya. Surabaya, 2005.

Raturi, A. S. and Evans, J. S.: Principal of Supply Chain Management. Thomson South-Western. Unated States of America, 2005.

Siagian, Y. M.: Aplikasi Supply Chain Management dalam Dunia Usaha. Grasindo, Jakarta, 2005.

Simichi-Levi et al.: Designing and Managing The Supply Chain (Concepts, Strategis, and Case Studies). International Edition. Mc. Graw-Hill, Singapore, 2000.

Van der Vorst, J. G. A. J.: Effective Food Supply Chains: Generating, Modelling and Evaluating Supply Chain Scenarios. PhD thesis. Wageningen University, 2000.

Van der Vorst, J. G. A. J.: Performance Measurement in Agrifood Supply Chain Networks : An Overview. In: Quantifying the agri-food supply chain/ Ondersteijn, dr.ir. C.J.M., Wijnands, ir. J.H.M., Huirne, prof.dr.ir R.B.M., Kooten, van prof.dr. O., . - Dordrecht : Springer/Kluwer, (Wageningen UR Frontis series 15, 2006.

Yandra, Marimin, Jamaran, I., Eriyatno, and Tamura, H.: An Integration of Multi-Objective Genetic Algorithm and Fuzzy Logic for Optimization of Agroindustrial Supply Chain Design, 2007.

Wong, W. P. and Wong K.Y.: Supply Chain Performance Measurement System Using DEA Modelling. Working Paper. 107(3), 361-381, 2007.

Some Information about ISSDA

The International Society for Sustainable Development and Agriculture (ISSDA) pursues the objective of sustainable development with the intention to achieve an enduring, peaceful and socially balanced future for all mankind. The starting point for the initiative was the Afro-Asian Studies Promotion Association (AASF), based in the university town of Goettingen, Germany. Ever since it was founded in 1957, it has developed an international network of qualified academics in many African and Asian countries, with regular and intensive exchanges of ideas. AASF has for many years organized seminars for students from African and Asian countries in Germany. The association gave particular emphasis in its meetings and publications to food security and sustainable development. In addition a group of international scientists created in Goettingen in 2007 a more focussed association, the International Foundation of Sustainable Development in Africa and Asia (IFSDAA). The founding members elected Prof. Dr. Hans Meliczek as IFSDAA president.

During the meeting of the General Assembly of IFSDAA held in Szeged in June 2010 the participants recommended to register the association as a non-profit association in the form of "eingetragener Verein" in Germany. In accordance with this request a new association called International Society for Sustainable Development and Agriculture (ISSDA) has been established. Its president is once more H. Meliczek.

Members of ISSDA form an international network of experts from different disciplines, who share their knowledge and experience in the field of development policies and development projects and are engaged in scientific exchange of experience across subject matters and generations. The purpose of the society will is achieved by:

- Regular consultations in the form of conferences, seminars and similar events,
- Initiating, supporting and implementing projects that aim at applying scientific-technical knowledge in the fields of agriculture, forestry, land use, resource management in land, water, flora and fauna, food security and renewable energy,
- Cooperation with national and international organizations as well as non-governmental organizations.

The society concentrates its activities on the following topics:

- Resource Management in Agriculture, Plant Nutrition and Rhizosphere, Cropping Systems, Water, Soils and Long Term Fertilization,
- Crop Improvement,
- Sustainability, Governance and Climate Change,
- Socio-economic Sustainability,
- Rural Sociology,
- Human Resource Management,
- Renewable Energy,
- Sustainable Development,
- Forestry and Resource Management,
- Animal and Human Health.

More information can be found on http://www.issda.de

www.ingramcontent.com/pod-product-compliance
Lightning Source LLC
Chambersburg PA
CBHW050911030726
47586CB00005B/1529